C000214519

Ocean Yachtmaster Exercises

Exercises in Celestial Navigation

Ocean Yachtmaster Exercises

Exercises in Celestial Navigation

Pat Langley-Price and Philip Ouvry

ADLARD COLES LIMITED
8 Grafton Street, London W1

Adlard Coles
William Collins Sons & Co. Ltd
8 Grafton Street, London W1X 3LA

First published in Great Britain by
Adlard Coles 1986
Reprinted 1989

Distributed in the United States of America
by Sheridan House, Inc.

Copyright © Sirius Sailing and Marine Limited 1986

British Library Cataloguing in Publication Data

Langley-Price, Pat
Ocean yachtmaster exercises: exercises in celestial navigation.
1. Yachts and yachting 2. Seamanship
I. Title II. Ouvry, Philip
623.88'223 GV813

ISBN 0-229-11792-9

Printed and bound in Great Britain by
Hartnolls Ltd, Bodmin, Cornwall

All rights reserved. No part of this publication may be reproduced, stored in a retrieval system, or transmitted, in any form or by any means, electronic, mechanical, photocopying, recording or otherwise, without the prior permission of the publisher.

Contents

Acknowledgements

Her Majesty's Stationery Office for permission to reproduce pages from the *Nautical Almanac* **and** *AP 3270 Sight Reduction Tables for Air Navigation Volumes 1 and 3*;

Ron Schaaf, Cdr Peter Linstead-Smith and the students of Chelsea-Westminster Institute for help with checking the problems.

Introduction

Ocean Yachtmaster Exercises contains a series of questions with worked answers to enable the student of celestial navigation to supplement his knowledge of the theory gained either from an instructional book or from classwork. It has been written, by the same authors, as a companion volume to *Ocean Yachtmaster* but the straightforward layout makes it complementary to any course of study. Although no lengthy explanations of method are given, the detailed answers are self-explanatory. A reminder of basic rules has been included at the beginning of some chapters.

Extracts from tables and sight reduction forms have been provided so that the only additional items required are plotting instruments and squared paper or a plotting sheet.

The worked examples include several methods of solving the PZX triangle. There are additional publications with alternative methods which are usually well explained and normally not dissimilar to at least one of the methods shown.

Times (twilight and meridian passage) are to the nearest minute, angles to one-tenth of a minute and distance to one-tenth of a nautical mile.

A complete list of symbols and abbreviations has been included.

All the questions have been used as class examples by the authors and are unambiguous and accurate. Nevertheless, the authors would welcome, through the publisher, any comments that might enable the improvement of future editions.

Symbols and Abbreviations

♈	Aries
+	Dead Reckoning Position
~	Difference Between
◬	Estimated Position
⊙	Observed Position (fix)
⟷	Position Line
◇	Preferred Star
—⋙—	Tidal Stream or Current
⋘—⋙	Transferred Position Line
A	Away (of Intercept)
a_0	Incremental Correction - Polaris
a_1	Incremental Correction - Polaris
a_2	Incremental Correction - Polaris
AA	Apparent Altitude
Add corrn	Additional Correction
Az	Azimuth (Bearing)
BST	British Summer Time
C lat	Chosen Latitude
C long	Chosen Longitude
CA	Calculated Altitude
CP	Chosen Position
CZD	Calculated Zenith Distance
Corrn	Correction
cos	Cosine
d	Day
d	Incremental Correction for Declination
D lat	Difference of Latitude
D long	Difference of Longitude
dist	Distance

DEC	Declination
Dep	Departure (D long × cos lat)
DR	Dead Reckoning Position
DWT	Deck Watch Time (12 Hour Clock Giving GMT)
E	East
EP	Estimated Position
FPA	First Point of Aries
GD	Greenwich Date
GHA	Greenwich Hour Angle
GM	Greenwich Meridian
GMT	Greenwich Mean Time
GP	Geographical Position
h	Hour
HA	Hour Angle
Hc	Altitude (Sight Reduction Tables)
HE	Height of Eye (dip)
HP	Horizontal Parallax (Moon Sights)
IE	Index Error (Sextant)
INT	Intercept
ITP	Intercept Terminal Position
Incre	Increment
k	Knot (1 Nautical Mile per Hour)
LHA	Local Hour Angle
LL	Lower Limb (Sun and Moon)
LMT	Local Mean Time
lat	Latitude
Log	Distance Travelled
long	Longitude
m	Minute
M	Nautical Mile
MA	Meridian Altitude
MP	Meridian Passage
N	North
OP	Observed Position
s	Second
S	South
SA	Sextant Altitude
SD	Semi-Diameter
SHA	Sidereal Hour Angle
sin	Sine

Symbols and Abbreviations

T	True (of Compass)
T	Towards (of Intercept)
TA	True Altitude
TZD	True Zenith Distance
UL	Upper Limb (Sun and Moon)
v	Incremental Correction for Hour Angle
W	West
Z	Azimuth Angle
ZD	Zenith Distance
Zn	Azimuth (Sight Reduction Tables)
ZT	Zone Time

Chapter One

Time

GMT = LMT + long W - long E (expressed as time)

Zone time +/- zone number

1.1 On 14 June in DR position 45°59'.1N 160°15'.1W, it is 1200 LMT. What is GMT?

1.2 It is 0448 LMT on 8 October. The DR position is 21°12'.4S 91°35'.1E. What is the GD?

1.3 In EP 40°34'.7N 167°30'.4W the LMT is 2010. The local date is 7 July. What is GMT?

1.4 On 27 May in DR position 44°30'.7N 3°29'.4W LMT is 1954. Check the GD and find GMT.

1.5 In DR position 35°14'.5S 82°44'.9E on 1 October the LMT is 0448. What is the GD?

1.6 On 3 April, what is the GMT and GD in zone +11 if the zone time is 0502?

1.7 Find GMT in zone -1 at 0358 zone time on 7 August. What is the GD?

1.8 In zone -6 on 21 November the zone time is 0431. Check the GD and find GMT.

1.9 If zone time is 1658 in zone -10 what is GMT?

1.10 On 7 June in zone +1, zone time is 1159. What is GMT?

1.11 In the forenoon of 9 July in zone +4 the ship's clock shows 8h 45m 15s. The deck watch, which is 6 seconds slow, shows 12h 45m 10s. What is GMT? Is the ship's clock showing the correct zone time?

1.12 On 20 June the chronometer, which is 2 seconds fast, shows 5h 06m 53s. The ship is in zone -11 and the ship's clock shows 4h 06m 50s in the morning. What is GMT? What is the GD?

1.13 A boat's DR position is 46°31'.7N 40°12'.1W. What time zone is she in?

1.14 On 7 June, a boat is in zone +12 sailing westwards. At 2350 zone time she is approaching the 180° meridian. What is the date and zone time 15 minutes later when she is in zone -12?

1.15 On 14 September (GD) at 1140 GMT a boat is in zone -12. At 1210 GMT she has crossed the 180° meridian. What is the local date? Is it necessary to alter the ship's clock or the chronometer?

Chapter Two

Rising and Setting Times

2.1 What is the GMT of civil twilight at dawn on 12 June in DR position 35°17'.6N 15°20'.8W?

2.2 Find the GMT of dusk twilight in preparation for evening sights on 7 October in DR position 30°24'.7N 20°45'.3W.

2.3 On 9 October when in DR position 42°45'.8S 160°01'.4E it is desired to know the GMT of dusk twilight in preparation for evening sights. When will this occur?

2.4 On 14 June when in DR position 20°34'.2N 151°17'.2W it is planned to take dawn sights. What is the GMT of morning twilight?

2.5 Find the GMT of evening twilight on 8 October in DR position 29°40'.3S 170°31'.2W.

2.6 What is the ZT of sunrise on 9 October in DR position 50°15'.4N 19°31'.7W? (Zone +1.)

2.7 On 13 June a boat is in DR position 45°40'.9N 7°41'.3W. What is the ZT of sunset? (Zone +1.)

2.8 At what ZT will sunrise occur on 7 October in DR position 32°04'.4S 162°01'.4E? (Zone -11.)

2.9 Find the ZT of sunset on 9 October in DR position 38°30'.7S 80°16'.9W. (Zone +5.)

2.10 What is the ZT of sunrise on 12 June in DR position 44°29'.7N 130°01'.7W? (Zone +9.)

2.11 Find the ZT of moonrise on 13 June in DR position 45°40'.0N 3°25'.0W. (Zone 0.)

2.12 At what ZT will moonrise occur on 15 June in DR position 45°42'.4N 159°25'.2E? (Zone -11.)

2.13 When in DR position 20°39'.4S 169°58'.4W it is required to know the ZT of moonrise and of moonset on 12 June. At what time will they occur? (Zone +11.)

2.14 What is the ZT of moonset on 14 June in DR 32°10'.1S 161°59'.4E? (Zone -11.)

2.15 When will moonrise occur in DR position 50°10'.3N 21°17'.8W on 14 June? (Zone +1.)

Chapter Three

Hour Angle and Declination

LHA = GHA (+SHA for a star) - long W + long E

3.1 What is the LHA and DEC of the Sun on 7 October at 10h 29m 15s GMT when in DR position 30°15'.4S 98°10'.1E?

3.2 Find the LHA and DEC of the Sun at 15h 16m 51s GMT on 13 June when in DR position 45°37'.0N 3°53'.0W.

3.3 On 14 June in DR position 45°59'.1N 179°50.3E the GHA of the Sun was 232°12'.3. Find the LHA to the nearest whole degree using a chosen longitude.

3.4 On 12 June when in DR position 45°58'.7N 120°17'.1W the GHA of the Sun was 82°21'.7. What was the LHA to the nearest whole degree using a chosen longitude?

3.5 What is the LHA and DEC of the Moon on 14 June in DR position 35°10'.7S 15°17'.4W at 16h 28m 05s GMT?

3.6 Find the LHA (to the nearest whole degree) and DEC of the Moon on 13 June at dusk twilight when in DR position 45°01'.3N 157°30'.2W.

3.7 On 12 June in DR position 40°05'.3N 18°29'.8W it is desired to know the LHA and DEC of Saturn at 21h 16m 10s GMT. (Use a chosen longitude.)

3.8 What is the LHA and DEC of Venus on 12 June in DR position 25°16'.1S 60°15'.0E at 13h 41m 10s GMT?

3.9 At dawn twilight on 7 October it is desired to take a sight of Mars in DR position 45°45'.3N 19°30'.1W. What will be the approximate LHA and DEC of Mars at that time?

3.10 On 7 October in DR position 49°50.6N 19°45'.4W Jupiter was observed at dusk twilight. What was the LHA and DEC at the time of the observation?

3.11 What will be the LHA of Aries at dawn twilight on 14 June in DR position 46°00'.6N 167°45'.0W?

3.12 On 7 October at 10h 29m 00s GMT when in DR position 30°21'.4S 80°30'.0W a sight of Pollux was obtained. What was the LHA and DEC of this star?

3.13 Find the LHA and DEC of Denebola on 13 June at dusk twilight when in DR position 45°58'.1N 167°30'.0W.

3.14 On 14 June when in DR position 45°54'.2N 158°45'.0E a dusk sight is to be taken of Dubhe. What will be the LHA and DEC?

3.15 At dawn twilight on 8 October when in DR position 25°29'.4S 160°29'.8E an observation is required of Canopus. What will be the LHA and DEC? (Use a chosen longitude.)

Chapter Four

True Altitude

4.1 On 13 June the sextant altitude of the upper limb of the Sun was 47°27'.4. Index error -1'.0. Height of eye 2.5m. What was the true altitude?

4.2 The sextant altitude of the lower limb of the Sun on 9 October was 33°06'.2. Index error 0'.9 on the arc. Height of eye 3.3m. Find the true altitude?

4.3 On 13 June at 22h 16m 00s GMT an observation of the lower limb of the Moon gave a sextant altitude of 28°15'.6. Index error 2'.0 off the arc. Height of eye 2.5m. Horizontal parallax 60.4. What was the true altitude?

4.4 On 22 October an observation of the upper limb of the Moon gave a sextant altitude of 22°14'.8. Index error -1'.5. Height of eye 2.5m. Horizontal parallax 56.1. Find the true altitude.

4.5 What was the true altitude of Jupiter on 31 May if the sextant altitude was 13°41'.7? Index error -0'.5. Height of eye 2.0m.

4.6 On 23 April the sextant altitude of Venus was 27°54'.0. Index error +1'.8. Height of eye 3.1m. Find the true altitude.

4.7 On 7 October a dawn sight was taken of Mars giving the following result: Sextant altitude 31°00'.7. Index error 1'.5 on the arc. Height of eye 3.0m. What was the true altitude?

4.8 At dusk on 14 June an observation of Saturn gave a sextant altitude of 35°43'.4. Index error 2'.1 off the arc. Height of eye 2.5m. Find the true altitude.

4.9 At dawn on 11 August, the sextant altitude of Aldebaran was 55°35'.2. Index error -1'.2. Height of eye 3.3m. What was the true altitude?

4.10 On 18 November the sextant altitude of Peacock was 52°58'.4. Index error +0'.9. Height of eye 2.7m. What was the true altitude?

4.11 On 30 June a dawn sight of Canopus gave a sextant altitude of 21°13'.8. Index error -1'.5. Height of eye 2.0m. Find the true altitude.

4.12 At dusk on 21 February, a sight taken of Betelgeuse gave a sextant altitude of 42°06'.0. Index error +2'.2. Height of eye 1.5m. What was the true altitude?

4.13 On 14 June a dawn observation of Capella gave a sextant altitude of 14°28'.1. Index error 1'.0 off the arc. Height of eye 3.1m. What was the true altitude?

4.14 What is the true altitude of Sirius on 7 October if a dawn sight gave a sextant altitude of 27°40'.9? Index error -1'.8. Height of eye 2.0m.

4.15 At dawn on 29 September a sight was taken of Diphda. The sextant altitude was 23°45'.9. Index error +1'.2. Height of eye 2.0m. What was the true altitude?

Chapter Five

Stars - AP3270, Volume 1

5.1 On 14 June when in DR position 45°40.6N 2°15'.0W it is desired to know which stars are available for morning sights.

(a) List these together with their altitudes and azimuths.

(b) Which are the brightest?

(c) Which give the best angle of cut?

5.2 When in DR position 45°45'.3N 19°30'.1W the following sights were taken at dawn twilight on 7 October:

Star	*DWT*	*Sextant altitude*
Dubhe	6h 54m 00s	49°51'.6
Mirfak	6h 54m 45s	57°34'.9
Sirius	6h 55m 15s	27°40'.9

Index error -1'.8. Height of eye 2.0m.

Find the intercept and azimuth of each star.

5.3 (a) List the stars available at dusk twilight on 7 October when in DR position 46°10'.4N 7°29'.9W.

(b) The three which gave the best angle of cut were chosen and the following sights taken:

Star	*DWT*	*Sextant altitude*
Arcturus	6h 28m 02s	26°32'.0
Altair	6h 28m 35s	51°19'.4
Mirfak	6h 29m 58s	17°08'.7

Index error -0'.8. Height of eye 2.5m.

Give the chosen position, intercept and azimuth of each star ready for plotting.

5.4 On 8 October the following observations were obtained at dawn twilight when in DR position 46°08'.4S 160°01'.7W:

Star	*DWT*	*Sextant altitude*
Suhail	3h 28m 00s	56°17'.7
Aldebaran	3h 28m 40s	24°48'.5
Achernar	3h 29m 12s	50°04'.6
Sirius	3h 29m 59s	58°56'.9

Index error 1'.2 off the arc. Height of eye 2.0m.

What is the length of the intercept and the azimuth of each star?

5.5 (a) List the stars available at dawn twilight on 8 October when in DR position 46°10'.4S 91°45'.1E.

(b) Which three give the best angle of cut?

(c) If more than three are chosen, upon what will that choice be based?

5.6 (a) On 14 June when in DR position 46°00'.6N 167°45'.0W it is proposed to take morning sights. Which stars will be available for use with AP 3270, Sight Reduction Tables for Air Navigation, Volume 1, Selected Stars?

(b) It was only possible to obtain sights of three of these stars as follows:

	Approximate bearing	*DWT*	*Sextant altitude*
Star 1	340° T	2h 40m 01s	43°11'.1
Star 2	210° T	2h 40m 50s	50°01'.0
Star 3	270° T	2h 41m 59s	62°37'.1

Index error 2'.1 off the arc. Height of eye 1.5m.

What is the intercept and azimuth of each star?

5.7 On the evening of 13 June when in DR position 45°58'.1N 167°30'.0W sights were taken of three stars. The times when these sights were taken together with their sextant altitudes are given below. Find the intercepts and azimuths ready for plotting.

	Approximate bearing	*DWT*	*Sextant altitude*
Star 1	170° T	7h 40m 00s	63°04'.0
Star 2	070° T	7h 40m 25s	39°59'.6
Star 3	320° T	7h 41m 48s	60°25'.6

Index error 1'.7 on the arc. Height of eye 2.5m.

5.8 At dawn twilight on 14 June when in DR position 45°59'.3N 159°06'.7E sights were taken of the stars tabulated below. Work out the intercept and azimuth of each.

Stars - AP 3270, Volume 1

Star	*DWT*	*Sextant altitude*
Enif	4h 54m 01s	52°37'.0
Alphecca	4h 54m 30s	25°10'.8
Rasalhague	4h 55m 05s	35°53'.8
Altair	4h 55m 59s	50°11'.3

Index error -1'.5. Height of eye 3.0m.

5.9 On 14 June when in DR position 45°54'.2N 158°45'.0E it is planned to take evening star sights. List the stars available with their altitudes and azimuths.

5.10 At dawn twilight on 8 October in DR position 46°05'.4S 82°45'.1E the following stars were observed:

Star	*DWT*	*Sextant altitude*
Suhail	11h 16m 03s	55°34'.1
Aldebaran	11h 17m 25s	25°04'.5
Achernar	11h 17m 51s	50°34'.3

Index error +1'.6. Height of eye 3.0m.

Give the intercepts and azimuths ready for plotting.

Chapter Six

Stars - AP3270, Volume 3

6.1 At dusk on 13 June in DR position 46°07'.9N 2°30'.4W sights of stars were taken at the following times:

Star	*GMT*
Alphecca	20h 40m 01s
Rasalhague	20h 40m 52s
Denebola	20h 41m 26s

Work out the calculated altitude and azimuth of each star.

6.2 On 7 October in DR position 46°15'.5S 91°30'.7W the following dawn sights were taken:

Star	*GMT*	*Sextant altitude*
Rigel	10h 54m 39s	51°14'.7
Menkar	10h 55m 09s	27°21'.3
Alphard	10h 55m 24s	30°48'.5

Index error +2'.7. Height of eye 3.1m.

Find the intercepts and azimuths ready for plotting.

6.3 When in DR position 45°57'.4N 14°30'.2W dawn sights were taken on 13 June giving the following results:

Star	*GMT*	*Sextant altitude*
Rasalhague	04h 28m 19s	36°15'.3
Altair	04h 28m 58s	50°13'.5
Alphecca	04h 29m 15s	25°22'.4

Index error 2'.0 off the arc. Height of eye 3.1m.

Give the chosen longitude, intercept and azimuth of each star.

6.4 On the morning of 7 October when in DR position 45°56'.9N 12°29'.8W the following stars were observed:

Stars - AP 3270, Volume 3

Star	*GMT*	*Sextant altitude*
Rigel	06h 28m 14s	32°39'.6
Procyon	06h 28m 51s	47°33'.4
Regulus	06h 29m 12s	34°56'.4

Index error +2'.9. Height of eye 3.0m.

What are the chosen longitudes, intercepts and azimuths of the above stars?

6.5 In DR position 45°55'.8S 100°15'.0W on 8 October sights were taken at evening twilight. The results are given below:

Star	*GMT*	*Sextant altitude*
Enif	01h 28m 02s	29°10'.5
Sabik	01h 28m 47s	44°06'.4
Zubenelgenubi	01h 29m 12s	20°47'.5

Index error +1'.1. Height of eye 1.5m.

Calculate the intercept and azimuth of each star.

6.6 At dusk on 12 June in DR position 45°48'.7N 17°44'.8W three star observations were obtained as follows:

Star	*GMT*	*Sextant altitude*
Spica	21h 40m 02s	32°47'.3
Pollux	21h 40m 37s	18°32'.5
Arcturus	21h 41m 11s	63°02'.1

Index error 2'.9 off the arc. Height of eye 2.0m.

Find the intercepts and azimuths of these stars.

6.7 On 12 June in DR position 46°19'.7N 20°29'.4W star sights were taken at dusk. The results are tabulated below:

Star	*GMT*	*Sextant altitude*
Alphecca	21h 54m 41s	62°28'.8
Rasalhague	21h 54m 57s	33°19'.4
Regulus	21h 55m 21s	31°05'.4

Index error +2'.2. Height of eye 2.0m.

Calculate the intercept and azimuth of each star.

6.8 At dawn on 8 October when in DR position 46°08'.4S 160°01'.7W it was only possible to observe the following two stars:

Star	*GMT*
Diphda	15h 28m 07s
Betelgeuse	15h 29m 10s

Do they give a good angle of cut?

6.9 The following observations were taken at dusk on 14 June in DR position 46°27'.4N 25°44'.8W:

Star	*GMT*	*Sextant altitude*
Denebola	22h 16m 03s	47°32'.9
Arcturus	22h 16m 37s	62°47'.9
Alphecca	22h 17m 18s	63°40'.1

Index error 0'.7 on the arc. Height of eye 2.5m.

What are the chosen longitudes, intercepts and azimuths of these stars?

6.10 When in DR position 45°40'.7S 154°58'.5E on 9 October, morning sights were taken as follows:

Star	*GMT*	*Sextant altitude*
Bellatrix	18h 28m 05s	37°33'.7
Procyon	18h 28m 50s	34°01'.1
Alphard	18h 29m 31s	31°18'.0

Index error +1'.4. Height of eye 2.5m.

Do the necessary calculations in preparation for plotting.

Chapter Seven

Planets

7.1 On the evening of 7 October at 9h 29m 12s DWT in DR position 45°33'.4S 40°09'.5W a sight was taken of Jupiter giving a sextant altitude of 41°25'.4. Index error 1'.0 on the arc. Height of eye 2.5m. What was the intercept and azimuth obtained from this sight?

7.2 At 3h 28m 17s DWT when in DR position 46°08'.4S 160°01'.7W on 8 October Venus was observed at dawn twilight giving a sextant altitude of 11°21'.0. Index error 2'.6 off the arc. Height of eye 1.5m. Find the intercept and azimuth ready for plotting.

7.3 A dusk observation of Saturn taken at 8h 29m 59s DWT on 14 June in DR position 45°40'.6N 2°15'.0W gave a sextant altitude of 35°56'.0. Index error -1'.0. Height of eye 2.5m. What was the chosen position, intercept and azimuth?

7.4 A morning sight of Mars taken at 06h 55m 10s GMT on 7 October in DR position 45°45'.3N 19°30'.1W gave a sextant altitude of 30°56'.9. Index error +2'.0. Height of eye 2.0m. Work out the intercept and azimuth.

7.5 When in DR position 46°00'.6N 167°45'.0W on 12 June an evening sight was taken of Venus at 07h 41m 59s GMT. The sextant altitude was 22°21'.3. Index error 1'.8 on the arc. Height of eye 3.2m. Calculate the intercept and azimuth.

7.6 On the morning of 8 October at 10h 41m 58s DWT when in DR position 46°10'.4S 91°45'.1E Venus was observed giving a sextant altitude of 11°48'.5. Index error 2'.0 on the arc. Height of eye 1.5m. Calculate the intercept and azimuth. What was the chosen position?

7.7 During dawn twilight on 8 October in DR position 46°05'.4S 82°45'.1E a sight was taken of Venus at 11h 17m 57s DWT giving a sextant altitude of 11°36'.3. Index error -1'.3. Height of eye 3.3m. Give the intercept and azimuth ready for plotting.

7.8 At 09h 29m 10s GMT on 14 June in DR position 45°31'.8N 165°00'.0E Saturn was observed during the evening giving a sextant altitude of 36°04'.4. Index error -1'.5. Height of eye 2.7m. Find the intercept and azimuth.

7.9 On 8 October when in DR position 45°32'.4S 151°45'.0E a dusk sight was taken of Jupiter at 08h 41m 50s GMT. The sextant altitude obtained was 41°05'.2. Index error 2'.6 off the arc. Height of eye 2.0m. What was the intercept and azimuth?

7.10 At dawn on 7 October in DR position 45°37'.8N 10°15'.2W Mars was observed at 06h 16m 50s GMT and the sextant altitude found to be 30°22'.2. Index error +1.2. Height of eye 3.0m. Calculate the intercept and azimuth.

Chapter Eight

Sun

8.1 On 12 June it is proposed to take an observation of the Sun as it transits the meridian. The boat's DR position at that time is expected to be 44°35'.3N 7°01'.0W. What will be the approximate GMT of meridian passage of the sun?

8.2 When in DR position 34°16'.7S 11°01'.0E on 12 June the upper limb of the Sun was observed at 11h 16m 02s GMT as it crossed the meridian giving a sextant altitude of 33°01'.4. Index error +0'.8. Height of eye 2.5m. Calculate the latitude obtained from this sight.

8.3 An observation of the Sun's lower limb was taken at meridian passage at 14h 16m 04s GMT on 22 January in DR position 23°21'.7N 31°04'.7W. The sextant altitude was 46°42'.1. Index error 3'.1 off the arc. Height of eye 2.5m. Find the observed latitude.

8.4 (a) On 24 January it is proposed to take a sight of the Sun at meridian passage. The DR position at that time is estimated to be 41°08'.1S 79°30'.4E. What will be the approximate time of the sight?

(b) A sight was taken at 06h 54m 20s GMT when the sextant altitude of the upper limb was 68°27'.4. Index error +0'.4. Height of eye 2.0m. Give the latitude obtained.

8.5 At 11h 28m 15s zone time on 7 October when in DR position 45°12'.6S 170°14'.9E (zone -11) a sight was taken of the Sun as it crossed the meridian. The sextant altitude of the upper limb was 50°19'.8. Index error -0'.9. Height of eye 2.0m. What was the observed latitude?

8.6 In DR position 45°37'.0N 3°53'.0W on 13 June at 15h 16m 51s GMT an observation of the Sun's upper limb was taken giving a sextant altitude of 47°27'.4. Index error -1'.0. Height of eye 2.5m. Find the intercept and azimuth.

8.7 On 23 January in DR position 45°51'.2S 160°31'.4W (zone +11) a sight was taken of the Sun's lower limb at 08h 55m 21s zone time. The sextant altitude was 44°42'.1. Index error -0'.7. Height of eye 2.5m. Calculate the intercept and azimuth.

8.8 On 12 June when in DR position 45°58'.7N 120°17'.1W (zone +8) the Sun's lower limb was observed at 09h 29m 10s zone time giving a sextant altitude of 52°02'.2. Index error -2'.7. Height of eye 2.0m. What was the intercept and azimuth?

8.9 On 24 January an afternoon sight of the Sun's upper limb was taken at 16h 40m 31s zone time. The DR position was 46°20'.3S 155°01'.4E (zone -10). The sextant altitude was 26°27'.1. Index error +1'.0. Height of eye 3.0m. Find the intercept and azimuth.

8.10 On 8 October at 14h 16m 23s zone time a sight was taken of the upper limb of the Sun when in DR position 46°01'.4S 151°25'.6W (zone +10). The sextant altitude was 39°53'.2. Index error 2'.5 on the arc. Height of eye 3.2m. Calculate the intercept and azimuth.

Chapter Nine

Moon

9.1 What will be the approximate GMT on 23 January when the Moon transits the meridian in DR position 30°12'.7S 10°25'.4W?

9.2 When will meridian passage of the Moon occur on 24 January in position 35°04'.7S 80°18'.1E?

9.3 On 22 January in DR position 24°55'.4N 27°04'.3W a sight was taken when the Moon was due south. The true altitude was 75°54'.2. What was the latitude?

9.4 (a) At what zone time will meridian passage of the Moon occur on 23 January in position 5°20'.4N 167°45'.2E?

(b) If the true altitude at the time of meridian passage was 82°19'.2, what was the latitude?

9.5 On 23 January in DR position 39°19'.4S 34°58'.7W the upper limb of the Moon was observed at meridian passage giving a sextant altitude of 34°34'.1. Index error +2'.1. Height of eye 2.9m. What was the observed latitude?

9.6 In zone -11 on 14 June in DR position 45°40'.3N 159°20'.1E a dusk sight was taken of the lower limb of the Moon at 20h 40m 07s zone time. The sextant altitude obtained was 23°49'.9. Index error 3'.3 off the arc. Height of eye 3.1m. Calculate the intercept and azimuth ready for plotting.

9.7 In DR position 46°20'.2N 167°20'.4W on 13 June a dusk sight of the Moon's lower limb was obtained at 07h 41m 38s GMT giving a sextant altitude of 20°42'.5. Index error 1'.4 off the arc. Height of eye 2.5m. Find the intercept and azimuth.

9.8 On the evening of 23 January when in DR position 45°32'.4S 80°16'.3E the Moon's upper limb was observed at 2h 54m 32s DWT giving a sextant altitude of 27°27'.3. Index error 1'.3 on the arc. Height of eye 2.7m. Give the intercept and azimuth.

9.9 When in DR position 46°27'.4S 59°10'.4W on 22 January an evening observation of the Moon's upper limb was taken at 00h 17m 41s GMT giving a sextant

altitude of 26°57'.6. Index error +2'.8. Height of eye 2.0m. What was the intercept and azimuth obtained from this sight?

9.10 On 12 June when in zone +11 in DR position 45°50'.8N 160°20'.4W a dusk sight was taken of the Moon's lower limb at 20h 16m 06s zone time giving a sextant altitude of 11°20'.1. Index error +2'.4. Height of eye 1.5m. Calculate the intercept and azimuth.

Chapter Ten

Polaris

10.1 On 14 June a dawn sight of Polaris is required. The boat's DR position at dawn twilight will be 45°40'.6N 2°15'.0W.

(a) What will be the approximate time to take the sight?

(b) What will be the approximate angle to set on the sextant?

10.2 On 7 October a boat steering a course of 190°C in DR position 40°10'.4N 19°29'.0W wished to check the deviation of the steering compass by using the azimuth of Polaris. A dusk sight was taken at 19h 17m 30s GMT when the bearing of Polaris on the steering compass was 019°C, variation 12°W. What was the deviation for the boat's heading?

10.3 When in DR position 46°10'.4N 7°29'.9W on 7 October an evening sight was taken of Polaris at 18h 28m 40s GMT giving a sextant altitude of 46°17'.3. Index error -0'.7. Height of eye 2.8m. What was the observed latitude?

10.4 A dawn sight of Polaris taken on 13 June at 07h 41m 03s GMT when in DR position 35°25'.8N 51°45'.1W gave a sextant altitude of 35°24'.1. Index error -2'.4. Height of eye 3.0m. Find the observed latitude.

10.5 On 13 June at dawn when in DR position 25°10'.7N 155°01'.9E an observation of Polaris taken at 6h 28m 12s DWT gave a sextant altitude of 25°21'.3. Index error 1'.5 off the arc. Height of eye 2.0m. What was the observed latitude?

10.6 When in DR position 19°40'.5N 50°06'.7W a dawn sight was taken of Polaris on 14 June at 08h 17m 01s GMT. The sextant altitude was 20°13'.6. Index error -0'.5. Height of eye 2.7m. Give the observed latitude.

10.7 A dusk sight of Polaris taken at 6h 54m 05s DWT on 7 October when in DR position 52°01'.3N 12°07'.4W gave a sextant altitude of 52°30'.7. Index error -1'.8. Height of eye 3.0m. Calculate the observed latitude.

10.8 On 8 October at 6h 55m 47s DWT a dusk sight of Polaris was taken when in DR position 49°59'.4N 15°10'.1W giving a sextant altitude of 50°05'.7.

Index error +4'.3. Height of eye 3.2m. Calculate the observed latitude.

10.9 When in DR position 40°01'.2N 160°12'.4E on 14 June a morning observation was taken of Polaris at 5h 17m 50s giving a sextant altitude of 40°10'.4. Index error +3'.8. Height of eye 2.5m. Find the observed latitude.

10.10 At 6h 29m 40s DWT on 7 October when in DR position 42°15'.7N 6°59'.4W a dusk sight was taken of Polaris. The sextant altitude was 42°10'.9. Index error 2'.1 on the arc. Height of eye 3.0m. What is the latitude?

Chapter Eleven

Plotting

These questions can be plotted on the appropriate plotting sheet or on squared paper. If the latter is used it is necessary to convert between difference of longitude (D long) and departure (Dep). This can be done by using a graph constructed for the required latitude (Fig. 11.1), by using traverse tables such as those contained in *Norie's Nautical Tables* or *Reed's Nautical Almanac*, or by applying the formulae (using tables or calculator):

$$\text{Dep} = \text{D long} \times \cos \text{lat}$$

$$\text{D long} = \frac{\text{Dep}}{\cos \text{lat}}$$

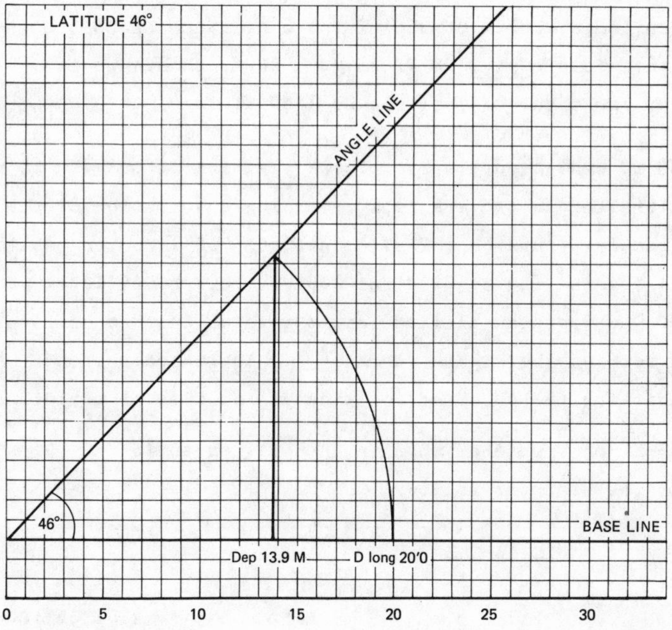

Figure 11.1 *To convert a D long of 20'.0 to Dep draw an arc radius 20'.0 from the base line to the angle line. From this point drop a perpendicular to the base line from which a Dep of 13.9 M can be read.*

11.1 At 1201 ZT on 14 June in DR position 46°18'.0N 179°41'.2E a sight taken of the Sun at its meridian passage gave a latitude of 46°17'.0N. The boat then steered a course of 195° T for a distance of 16 M when at 1645 ZT a Sun sight was taken giving the following: intercept 10'.3 T, azimuth 274°, chosen position 46°N 179°47'.7E. What was the boat's observed position at 1645 ZT?

11.2 On 28 January at 0800 ZT when in DR position 33°43'.0S 11°03'.6E a morning Sun sight was taken giving an intercept of 12'.0 A and an azimuth of 093° from a chosen position of 34°S 11°15'.9E. The boat then sailed on for a distance of 24.5 M on a course of 190° T until 1229 ZT, when the latitude by meridian altitude was determined to be 34°11'.5S. Plot the observed position at 1229 ZT.

11.3 On 23 January in DR position 29°50'.4S 160°40'.4E a boat was on passage from Fiji to Sydney. A morning Sun sight was taken at 0745 ZT giving: intercept 18'.1 A, azimuth 097°, chosen position 30°S 160°54'.4E. The boat then sailed on for 22.5 M on a course of 242° T until 1231 ZT when latitude by meridian altitude was found to be 30°01'.0S. What was the observed position at 1231 ZT?

11.4 On 28 March a boat was sailing from the Canary Islands to Guadeloupe. At 1147 ZT in DR position 19°08'.6N 40°35'.7W a sight was taken of the Sun as it crossed the meridian from which the latitude was determined to be 19°06'.8N. The boat then sailed a course of 266° T for a distance of 16.8 M when at 1550 ZT a Sun sight gave: intercept 3'.8 T, azimuth 262°, chosen position 19°N 40°55'.0W. Plot the observed position at 1550 ZT.

11.5 At 0808 ZT on 2 August a boat in DR position 34°59'.4N 15°01'.8W on passage from Gibraltar to Madiera took a morning observation of the Sun giving the following result: intercept 7'.7 A, azimuth 095°, chosen position 35°N 14°56'.4W. The log reading at 0808 was 365.0. Four hours later when the log reading was 389.0 a meridian altitude sight gave a latitude of 34°47'.2N. The course steered between the sights was 245° T. Estimated current: set 215° T, rate 0.5 k. What was the observed position at the time of meridian passage?

11.6 At 0455 ZT on 7 October when in DR position 46°15'.5S 91°30'.7W sights were taken of three stars as follows:

Star	*Intercept*	*Azimuth*	*Chosen longitude*
Rigel	12'.5 A	346°	91°44'.9W
Menkar	21'.0 A	311°	91°57'.2W
Alphard	2'.5 T	068°	91°41'.0W

Chosen latitude 46°S.

What was the observed position at 0455 ZT?

11.7 At 0429 ZT on 8 October a boat on a course of 110° T was in DR position 46°08'.4S 160°01'.7W when the following dawn sights were taken:

Star	*Intercept*	*Azimuth*	*Chosen longitude*	*ZT*	*Log*
Sirius	5'.0 A	023°	160°11'.6W	0429	900.2
Achernar	6'.0 T	229°	159°59'.8W	0435	901.4
Aldebaran	6'.9 A	339°	159°51'.8W	0440	902.5
Suhail	7'.5 A	103°	159°41'.7W	0448	904.1

Chosen latitude 46°S.

What was the observed position at 0448 ZT?

11.8 At 2006 ZT on 24 January in DR position 35°08'.3S 160°08'.4E the following sights were taken:

Star	*Intercept*	*Azimuth*	*Chosen longitude*
Aldebaran	3'.2 A	012°	159°52'.8E
Canopus	10'.2 T	136°	159°47'.7E
Fomalhaut	13'.5 A	251°	159°40'.2E
Moon	Latitude by meridian altitude		35°04'.8S

Chosen latitude 35°S.

Find the observed position at 2006 ZT.

11.9 At 0449 on 18 May a boat on passage from Honolulu to Hong Kong was in DR position 25°40'.6N 150°28'.7E when the following sights were taken:

Star	*Intercept*	*Azimuth*	*Chosen longitude*
Alpheratz	24'.8 A	073°	150°50'.0E
Nunki	24'.0 T	206°	150°38'.9E
Vega	7'.8 A	305°	150°36'.0E
Polaris	Observed latitude		25°37'.8N

Chosen latitude 26°N.

What was the observed position at 0449 ZT?

11.10 At 1913 ZT on 30 April a boat on passage from San Francisco to Panama was in DR position 29°19'.2N 123°07'.6W when the following sights were taken:

Star	*Intercept*	*Azimuth*	*Chosen longitude*
Venus	19'.4 T	285°	122°46'.3W
Sirius	3'.0 A	227°	122°45'.2W
Arcturus	5'.4 A	081°	122°52'.7W
Capella	17'.8 T	310°	122°56'.4W
Alphard	21'.5 A	181°	123°00'.7W
Polaris	Observed latitude		29°21'.4N

Chosen latitude 29°N.

Find the observed position at 1913 ZT.

Chapter Twelve

Ocean Passage Making

12.1 (a) On 7 October a boat is on passage from Falmouth to the Canary Islands. It is planned to take dusk sights. If the DR position at dusk is estimated to be 46°29'.1N 10°31'.2W, which stars will be available for use with AP 3270, Volume 1? Give their approximate altitudes and azimuths.

(b) At 1740 ZT the boat took the following sights in EP 46°30'.0N 10°29'.8W:

Star	DWT	Sextant altitude
Mirfak	6h 40m 10s	17°18'.4
Altair	6h 40m 31s	51°01'.2
Arcturus	6h 41m 20s	26°10'.3
Polaris	6h 41m 50s	46°14'.6

Index error +2'.0. Height of eye 2.5m. Log reading 302.0.

Plot the observed position at 1740 ZT.

(c) From the 1740 position the boat steered a course of 195° T until 0516 ZT on 8 October, when the following sights were taken:

Star	DWT	Sextant altitude
Dubhe	6h 16m 25s	49°52'.2
Sirius	6h 16m 50s	27°40'.6
Mirfak	6h 17m 15s	57°22'.0
Venus	6h 17m 55s	31°35'.1

Log reading 348.5. Current 180° T 0.5 k.

Plot the observed position at 0516 ZT.

(d) The boat continued on a course of 195° T, with an estimated current of 180° T 0.5 k. At 0717 ZT, log 356.5, a sight of the Sun's lower limb was taken giving a sextant altitude of 13°48'.1. At the time of the sight the deck watch showed 8h 17m 40s. Continuing on the same course and experiencing the same current, at 1131 ZT, log 373.5, a sight was taken of the upper limb of the Sun at meridian passage giving a sextant altitude of 39°19'.6. Plot the observed position at 1131 ZT.

(e) From a position 46°N 10°40'W what would be the great circle distance and initial course to Las Palmas, Canary Islands (28°08'N 15°40'W)?

12.2 (a) At 0328 ZT on 12 June a boat on passage from Yokohama to San Francisco is in DR position 46°30'.0N 150°14'.8W when the following sights are taken:

Star	*DWT*	*Sextant altitude*
Polaris	1h 28m 01s	46°38'.7
Enif	1h 28m 30s	51°31'.2
Rasalhague	1h 28m 51s	36°55'.9
Alphecca	1h 29m 25s	26°23'.2
Altair	1h 29m 57s	50°09'.5

Index error +2'.9. Height of eye 2.0m. Log 473.2.

Plot the observed position at 0328 ZT.

(b) The boat then sailed on a course of 110° T, current estimated to be 090° T 0.5 k. At 0655, log 492.2, a sight of the Sun's LL gave a sextant altitude of 26°02'.0. At the time of the sight the deck watch showed 4h 55m 49s. The boat continued on on the same course until 1155 ZT, log 524.2, when a meridian altitude of the Sun's UL was taken giving a sextant altitude of 67°09'.9. What was the OP at 1155 ZT?

(c) The boat continued on the same course until 1500 ZT, log 542.2, when a sight of the Sun's LL was taken at a DWT of 1h 00m 00s giving a SA of 45°51'.9. Plot the observed position at 1500.

(d) The boat continued on the same course until 2016, log 573.0, when the following dusk sights were taken:

Body	*DWT*	*Sextant altitude*
Moon LL	6h 16m 05s	12°23'.2
Saturn	6h 16m 40s	35°44'.6
Deneb	6h 16m 55s	23°50'.6
Arcturus	6h 17m 10s	62°51'.9
Pollux	6h 17m 35s	18°40'.6

Plot the observed position at 2016 ZT.

(e) What has been the mean current between 0328 ZT and 2016 ZT?

(f) What is the great circle distance and initial course from the 2016 position to Clipperton Island (10°25'N 109°33'W)?

Sight Reduction Forms

AP 3270 Vol. 1 STARS

DR ______________________ DATE ______________________

Initial Plan: Twilight LMT d

DR long +W/-E ________

________ GMT d

	Star	Hc	Zn

GHA Aries h

Increment m s ________

DR long ________

LHA Aries ________

Sights taken:

Star	________	________	________
GMT	________	________	________
GHA Aries h			
Increment m s	________	m s ________	m s ________
C long -W/+E	________	________	________
LHA Aries	________	________	________
C Lat	________		
Hc	________	________	________
Zn	________	________	________
SA			
IE	________	________	________
Dip	________	________	________
AA			
Corrn.	________	________	________
TA			
CA	________	________	________
INTERCEPT	________	________	________

AP 3270 Vol. 3 STARS

DR ______________________ DATE ______________________

Twilight LMT d

DR long +W/-E ________

________ GMT d

Star ____________ GMT ____________

SHA star

GHA Aries h

Increment m s ____________

GHA star

C long -W/+E ____________

LHA star ____________ DEC ____________

C lat ____________

Hc d Z Zn

____

____

SA

IE ____________

Dip ____________

AA

Corrn. ____________

TA

CA ____________

INTERCEPT ____________

AP 3270 Vol. 3 PLANETS

DR ______________________ DATE ______________________

GMT ______________________

PLANET ______________________

GHA h DEC

Increment m s d ______________

v ______________

C long -W/+E ______________

LHA ______________

C lat ______________

Hc d Z Zn

____

____

SA

IE ______________

Dip ______________

AA

Corrn. ______________

*Add Corrn ______________ *Venus and Mars only

TA

CA ______________

INTERCEPT ______________

LATITUDE BY POLARIS

DR ______________________ DATE ______________________

Twilight LMT d
DR long +W/-E ________
________ GMT d

GHA Aries h
Increment m s ____________

DR long -W/+E ____________
LHA Aries ____________

SA
IE ____________

Dip ____________
AA
Corrn. ____________
TA
a_0
a_1
a_2 ____________

-1° ____________
LATITUDE ____________

AP 3270 Vol. 3 SUN

DR ____________________ DATE ____________________

GMT ____________________

GHA h

Increment m s ____________

C long +W/-E ____________

LHA ____________

C lat ____________

DEC

d ____________

____

Hc d Z Zn

____

____

SA

IE ____________

Dip ____________

AA

Corrn. UL/LL ____________

TA

CA ____________

INTERCEPT ____________

APPENDIX E

LATITUDE BY MERIDIAN ALTITUDE

SUN

DR ______________________ DATE ______________________

MP | LMT d
DR long +W/-E ________
________ GMT d

DEC
d ____________
____

SA
IE ____________
Dip ____________
AA
Corrn. UL/LL ____________
TA
From 90° ____________
TZD
DEC ____________
LATITUDE ____________

AP 3270 Vol. 3 MOON

DR ______________________ DATE ______________________

GMT ______________________

GHA h | DEC

Increment m s | d ____________

v ____________ | ____________

C long -W/+E ____________

LHA ____________ | HP ____________

	Hc	d	Z	Zn
	____________			
	____________			

SA

IE ____________

Dip ____________

AA

Corrn.

HP UL/LL ____________

-30' UL ____________

TA

CA ____________

INTERCEPT ____________

LATITUDE BY MERIDIAN ALTITUDE
MOON

DR ______________________ DATE ______________________

h m

MP LMT d (long E use the previous day
MP ________ LMT d long W use the following day)

DD ________

$\frac{\quad}{360}$ X = m

h m

MP LMT at GM d
Long corrn. +W/-E ________ LMT at DR d
Long as time +W/-E ________
________ GMT at DR d

DEC
d ________
____

SA
IE ________
Dip ________
AA
Corrn.
HP UL/LL ________
-30' UL ________
TA
From 90° ________
TZD
DEC ________
LATITUDE ________

Answers

CHAPTER 1

1.1

	h m	
	12 00	LMT 14d
Long W	+10 41	
	22 41	**GMT 14d**

1.2

	h m	
	04 48	LMT 8d
Long E	-6 06	
	22 42	**GMT Greenwich date 7 October.**

1.3

	h m	
	20 10	LMT 7d
Long W	+11 10	
	07 20	**GMT 8d**

1.4

	h m	
	19 54	LMT 27d
Long W	+14	
	20 08	**GMT Greenwich date 27 May.**

1.5

	h m	
	04 48	LMT 1d
Long E	-5 31	
	23 17	**GMT Greenwich date 30 September.**

1.6

	h m	
	05 02	ZT 3d
Zone +11	+11	
	16 02	**GMT Greenwich date 3 April.**

1.7

	h m	
	03 58	ZT 7d
Zone -1	-1	
	02 58	**GMT Greenwich date 7 August.**

1.8

	h m
	04 31 ZT 21d
Zone -6	-6
	22 31 GMT Greenwich date 20 November.

1.9

	h m
	16 58 ZT
Zone -10	-10
	06 58 GMT

1.10

	h m
	11 59 ZT 7d
Zone +1	+1
	12 59 GMT 7d

1.11

	h m s
Deck watch	12 45 10
6s slow	+6
	12 45 16 DWT (corrected)

	h m s
ship's clock	8 45 15 ZT 9d
Zone +4	+4
	12 45 15 GMT 9d

The ship's clock is 1s slow. The correct zone time is 08h 45m 16s.

1.12

	h m s
Chronometer	5 06 53
2s fast	-2
	5 06 51 chronometer time (corrected)

	h m s
Ship's clock	4 06 50 ZT 20d
Zone -11	-11
	17 06 50 GMT 19d

Correct GMT is 17h 06m 51s. Greenwich date 19 June.

1.13 **Zone +3.**

1.14

	h m
	23 50 ZT 7d
Zone +12	+12
	11 50 GMT 8d

15m later

	h m
	12 05 GMT 8d
Zone -12	+12
	00 05 ZT 9d

Local date 9 June. Zone time 0005.

1.15

	h m	
	11 40	GMT 14d
Zone -12	+12	
	23 40	**ZT** 14d

	h m	
	12 10	GMT 14d
Zone +12	-12	
	00 10	**ZT** 14d

The local date remains 14 September. The ship's clock is unaltered. The chronometer is never altered at sea.

CHAPTER 2

Usually only approximate times are needed for rising and setting phenomena and no allowance has been made for the fact that sunrise, sunset and twilight are tabulated tri-daily. The error incurred will not exceed 2m. Interpolation between latitudes has been done. Twilight refers to the tabulated civil twilight.

2.1

	h m	
Dawn twilight	04 15	LMT 12d
Long W as time	+1 01	
	05 16	**GMT** 12 d

2.2

	h m	
Dusk twilight	18 02	LMT 7d
Long W as time	+1 23	
	19 25	**GMT** 7d

2.3

	h m	
Dusk twilight	18 43	LMT 9d
Long E as time	-10 40	
	08 03	**GMT** 9d

2.4

	h m	
Dawn twilight	04 55	LMT 14d
Long W as time	+10 05	
	15 00	**GMT** 14d

2.5

	h m	
Dusk twilight	18 29	LMT 8d
Long W as time	+11 22	
	05 51	**GMT** 9d

2.6

	h m	
Sunrise	06 10	LMT 9d
Long W as time	+1 18	
	07 28	GMT 9d
Zone +1	-1	
	06 28	**ZT** 9d

2.7

	h m	
Sunset	19 50	LMT 13d
Long W as time	+31	
	20 21	GMT 13d
Zone +1	-1	
	19 21	**ZT** 13d

2.8

	h m	
Sunrise	05 30	LMT 7d
Long E as time	-10 48	
	18 42	GMT 6d
Zone -11	+11	
	05 42	**ZT** 7d

2.9

	h m	
Sunset	18 11	LMT 9d
Long W as time	+5 21	
	23 32	GMT 9d
Zone +5	-5	
	18 32	**ZT** 9d

2.10

	h m	
Sunrise	04 15	LMT 12d
Long W as time	+8 40	
	12 55	GMT 12d
Zone +9	-9	
	03 55	**ZT** 12 d

2.11

	h m
Moonrise 14d	07 29
Moonrise 13d	-06 16
Daily difference	1 13 = 73m

$\frac{3.4}{360} \times 73 = 0.69$ (use 1m)

	h m	
Moonrise	06 16	LMT 13d at GM
Corrn for long W	+1	
	06 17	LMT 13d at DR
Long W as time	+14	
	06 31	GMT 13d at DR
Zone 0	0	
	06 31	**ZT** 13d at DR

2.12

	h m	
Moonrise 15d	08 48	
Moonrise 14d	-07 29	
Daily difference	1 19 = **79m**	

$\frac{159.42}{360} \times 79 = 35m$

	h m	
Moonrise	08 48	LMT 15d at GM
Corrn for long E	-35	
	08 13	LMT 15d at DR
Long E as time	-10 38	
	21 35	GMT 14d at DR
Zone -11	+11	
	08 35	**ZT** 15d at DR

2.13

	h m	
Moonrise 13d	08 50	
Moonrise 12d	-07 47	
Daily difference	1 03 = 63m	

$\frac{169.97}{360} \times 63 = 30m$

	h m	
Moonrise	07 47	LMT 12d at GM
Corrn for long W	+30	
	08 17	LMT 12d at DR
Long W as time	+11 20	
	19 37	GMT 12d at DR
Zone +11	-11	
	08 37	**ZT** 12d at DR

	h m	
Moonset 13d	20 01	
Moonset 12d	-18 55	
Daily difference	1 06 = 66m	

$\frac{169.97}{360} \times 66 = 31m$

	h m	
Moonset	18 55	LMT 12d at GM
Corrn for long W	+31	
	19 26	LMT 12d at DR
Long W as time	+11 20	
	06 46	GMT 13d at DR
Zone +11	-11	
	19 46	**ZT** 12d at DR

2.14

	h m
Moonset 14d	20 44
Moonset 13d	-19 34
Daily difference	1 10 = 70m

$\frac{161.99}{360} \times 70 = 31m$

	h m	
Moonset	20 44	LMT 14d at GM
Corrn for long E	-31	
	20 13	LMT 14d at DR
Long E as time	-10 48	
	09 25	GMT 14d at DR
Zone -11	+11	
	20 25	**ZT** 14d at DR

2.15

	h m
Moonrise 15d	08 32
Moonrise 14d	-07 10
Daily difference	1 22 = 82

$\frac{21.3}{360} \times 82 = 5m$

	h m	
Moonrise	07 10	LMT 14d at GM
Corrn for long W	+5	
	07 15	LMT 14d at DR
Long W as time	+1 25	
	08 40	GMT 14d at DR
Zone +1	-1	
	07 40	**ZT** 14d at DR

CHAPTER 3

3.1	GHA Sun 10h	333°00'.2	**DEC**	S5°21'.2
	Incre 29m 15s	+7°18'.8	d 1.0	+0'.5
	GHA Sun	340°19'.0		**S5°21'.7**
	DR long E	+98°10'.1		
		438°29'.1		
	-360°	-360°		
	LHA Sun	**78°29'.1**		
3.2	GHA Sun 15h	45°01'.4	**DEC**	N23°12'.1
	Incre 16m 51s	+4°12'.8	d 0.1	0'.0
	GHA Sun	49°14'.2		**N23°12'.1**
	DR long W	-3°53'.0		
	LHA Sun	**45°21'.2**		
3.3	GHA Sun	232°12'.3		
	C long E	+179°47'.7		
		412°		
	-360°	-360°		
	LHA Sun	**52°**		

3.4	GHA Sun	82°21'.7		
	+360	+360°		
	GHA Sun	442°21'.7		
	C long W	-120°21'.7		
	LHA Sun	**322°**		

3.5	GHA Moon 16h	7°59'.9	**DEC**	N21°09'.9
	Incre 28m 05s	+6°42'.1	d 8.0	-3'.8
	v 5.2	+2'.5		**N21°06'.1**
	GHA Moon	14°44'.5		
	+360°	+360°		
		374°44'.5		
	DR long W	-15°17'.4		
	LHA Moon	**359°27 .1**		

3.6		h m		
	Dusk twilight	20 25 LMT 13d		
	Long W as time	+10 30		
		06 55 GMT 14d		
	GHA Moon 06h	224°03'.5	**DEC**	N22°22'.1
	Incre 55m	+13°07'.4	d 6.6	-6'.1
	v 4.3	4'.0		**N22°16'.0**
	GHA Moon	237°14'.9		
	DR long W	-157°14'.9		
	LHA Moon	**80°**		

3.7	GHA Saturn 21h	8°39'.6	**DEC**	**S8°18'.7**
	Incre 16m 10s	+4°02'.5	d 0.0	
	v 2.5	+0'.7		
	GHA Saturn	12°42'.8		
	+360°	+360°		
		372°42'.8		
	C long W	-18°42'.8		
	LHA Saturn	**354°**		

3.8	GHA Venus 13h	326°00'.6	**DEC**	N20°51'.4
	Incre 41m 10s	+10°17'.5	d 0.7	-0'.5
	v 0.0	0'.0		**N20°50'.9**
	GHA Venus	336°18'.1		
	DR long E	+60°15'.0		
		396°33'.1		
	-360°	-360°		
	LHA Venus	**36°33'.1**		

3.9

	h m		
Dawn twilight	05 36 LMT 7d		
Long W as time	+01 18		
	06 54 GMT 7d		
GHA Mars 06h	308°28'.6	**DEC**	N11°05'.4
Incre 54m	+13°30'.0	d 0.6	-0'.5
v 1.0	+0'.9		**N11°04'.9**
GHA Mars	321°59'.5		
DR long W	-19°30'.1		
LHA Mars	**302°29'.4**		

3.10

	h m		
Dusk twilight	17 57 LMT 7d		
Long W as time	+1 19		
	19 16 GMT 7d		
GHA Jupiter 19h	54°44'.6	**DEC**	S21°08'.5
Incre 16m	+4°00'.0	d 0.1	0'.0
v 2.0	+0'.6		**S21°08'.5**
GHA Jupiter	58°45'.2		
DR long W	-19°45'.4		
LHA Jupiter	**38°59'.8**		

3.11

	h m
Dawn twilight	03 30 LMT 14d
Long W as time	+11 11
	14 41 GMT 14d
GHA Aries 14h	112°18'.0
Incre 40m	+10°16'.7
GHA Aries	122°34'.7
+360°	+360°
	482°34'.7
DR long W	-167°45'.0
LHA Aries	**314°49'.7**

3.12

SHA Pollux	243°55'.5	**DEC**	**N28°04'.0**
GHA Aries 10h	+165°29'.1		
Incre 29m	+7°16'.2		
GHA Pollux	416°40'.8		
DR long W	-80°30'.0		
LHA Pollux	**336°10'.8**		

3.13

	h m		
Dusk twilight	20 31 LMT 13d		
Long W as time	+11 10		
	07 41 GMT 14d		
SHA Denebola	182°57'.0	**DEC**	**N14°40'.1**
GHA Aries 07h	+7°00'.7		
Incre 41m	+10°16'.7		
GHA Denebola	200°14'.4		
DR long W	-167°30'.0		
LHA Denebola	**32°44'.4**		

3.14

	h m		
Dusk twilight	20 30 LMT 14d		
Long E as time	-10 35		
	09 55 GMT 14d		
SHA Dubhe	194°19'.7	**DEC**	**N61°50'.8**
GHA Aries 09h	+37°05'.7		
Incre 55m	+13°47'.3		
GHA Dubhe	245°12'.7		
DR long E	+158°45'.0		
	403°57'.7		
-360°	-360°		
LHA Dubhe	**43°57'.7**		

3.15

	h m		
Dawn twilight	05 10 LMT 8d		
Long E as time	-10 42		
	18 28 GMT 7d		
SHA Canopus	264°06'.2	**DEC**	**S52°40'.8**
GHA Aries 18h	+285°48'.8		
Incre 28m	+7°01'.1		
GHA Canopus	556°56'.1		
C long E	+160°03'.9		
	717°		
-360°	-360°		
LHA Canopus	**357°**		

CHAPTER 4

4.1

SA	47°27'.4
IE	-1'.0
	47°26'.4
Dip	-2'.8
AA	47°23'.6
Corrn June UL	-16'.7
TA	**47°06'.9**

4.2

SA	33°06'.2
IE	-0'.9
	33°05'.3
Dip	-3'.2
AA	33°02'.1
Corrn Oct LL	+14'.8
TA	**33°16'.9**

4.3

SA	28°15'.6
IE	+2'.0
	28°17'.6
Dip	-2'.8
AA	28°14'.8
Corrn	+59'.7
HP LL 60.4	+8'.1
TA	**29°22'.6**

4.4

SA	22°14'.8
IE	-1'.5
	22°13'.3
Dip	-2'.8
AA	22°10'.5
Corrn	+61'.7
HP UL 56.1	+2'.6
	23 14'.8
-30' for UL	-30'.0
TA	**22 44'.8**

4.5

SA	13°41'.7
IE	-0'.5
	13°41'.2
Dip	-2'.5
AA	13°38'.7
Corrn	-3'.9
TA	**13°34'.8**

4.6

SA	27°54'.0
IE	+1'.8
	27°55'.8
Dip	-3'.1
AA	27°52'.7
Corrn	-1'.8
	27°50'.9
Add corrn	+0'.1
TA	**27°51'.0**

4.7

SA	31°00'.7
IE	-1'.5
	30°59'.2
Dip	-3'.0
AA	30°56'.2
Corrn	-1'.6
	30°54'.6
Add corrn	+0'.1
TA	**30°54'.7**

4.8

SA	35°43'.4
IE	+2'.1
	35°45'.5
Dip	-2'.8
AA	35°42'.7
Corrn	-1'.3
TA	**35°41'.4**

4.9

SA	55°35'.2
IE	-1'.2
	55°34'.0
Dip	-3'.2
AA	55°30'.8
Corrn	-0'.7
TA	**55°30'.1**

4.10

SA	52°58'.4
IE	+0'.9
	52°59'.3
Dip	-2'.9
AA	52°56'.4
Corrn	-0'.7
TA	**52°55'.7**

4.11

SA	21°13'.8
IE	-1'.5
	21°12'.3
Dip	-2'.5
AA	21°09'.8
Corrn	-2'.5
TA	**21°07'.3**

4.12

SA	42°06'.0
IE	+2'.2
	42°08'.2
Dip	-2'.2
AA	42°06'.0
Corrn	-1'.1
TA	**42°04'.9**

4.13

SA	14°28'.1
IE	+1'.0
	14°29'.1
Dip	-3'.1
AA	14°26'.0
Corrn	-3'.7
TA	**14°22'.3**

4.14

SA	27°40'.9
IE	-1'.8
	27°39'.1
Dip	-2'.5
AA	27°36'.6
Corrn	-1'.8
TA	**27°34'.8**

4.15

SA	23°45'.9
IE	+1'.2
	23°47'.1
Dip	-2'.5
AA	23°44'.6
Corrn	-2'.2
TA	**23°42'.4**

CHAPTER 5

5.1

	h m
Dawn twilight	03 32 LMT 14d
Long W as time	+9
	03 41 GMT 14d

GHA Aries 03h	306°50'.9
Incre 41m	+10°16'.7
GHA Aries	317°07'.6
DR long W	-2°15'.0
LHA Aries	**314°52'.6** (use 315°)

(a) **Stars available:**

	Hc	Zn
CAPELLA	**14°22'**	**037°**
◇ **Hamal**	**25°42'**	**082°**
Alpheratz	**49°49'**	**098°**
Enif	**52°38'**	**162°**
◇ **ALTAIR**	**49°55'**	**207°**
VEGA	**62°46'**	**268°**
◇ **Kochab**	**43°12'**	**338°**

(b) The brightest stars are tabulated **in capital letters.**

(c) **The diamond (◇) indicates the stars which will give the best angle of cut if three are used.**

5.2

	h m
Dawn twilight	05 36 LMT 7d
Long W as time	+1 18
	06 54 GMT 7d

	Dubhe	Mirfak	Sirius
GMT	06h 54m 00s	06h 54m 45s	06h 55m 15s
GHA Aries 06h	105°19'.2	105°19'.2	105°19'.2
Incre	+13°32'.2	+13°43'.5	+13°51'.0
GHA Aries	118°51'.4	119°02'.7	119°10'.2
C long W	-19°51'.4	-19°02'.7	-19°10'.2
LHA Aries	99°	100°	100°
Hc	49°48'	57°24'	27°18'
Zn	**042°**	**295°**	**179°**
SA	49°51'.6	57°34'.9	27°40'.9
IE and dip	-4'.3	-4'.3	-4'.3
AA	49°47'.3	57°30'.6	27°36'.6
Corrn	-0'.8	-0'.6	-1'.8
TA	49°46'.5	57°30'.0	27°34'.8
CA	49°48'.0	57°24'.0	27°18'.0
Intercept	**1'.5** A	**6'.0** T	**16'.8** T

5.3

	h m
Dusk twilight	17 58 LMT 7d
Long W as time	+30
	18 28 GMT 7d

GHA Aries 18h	285°48'.8
Incre 28m	+7°01'.1
GHA Aries	292°49'.9
DR long W	-7°29'.9
LHA Aries	285°20'.0 (use 285°)

(a) **Stars available:**

	Hc	Zn
◇ **Mirfak**	**16°41'**	**033°**
Alpheratz	**29°07'**	**077°**
◇ **ALTAIR**	**51°19'**	**160°**
Rasalhague	**51°58'**	**215°**
◇ **ARCTURUS**	**26°37'**	**271°**
Alkaid	**39°39'**	**304°**
Kochab	**51°16'**	**337°**

(b)

	Arcturus	Altair	Mirfak
GMT	18h 28m 02s	18h 28m 35s	18h 29m 58s
GHA Aries 18h	285°48'.8	285°48'.8	285°48'.8
Incre	+7°01'.7	+7°09'.9	+7°30'.7
GHA Aries	292°50'.5	292°58'.7	293°19'.5
C long W	-7°50'.5	-7°58'.7	-7°19'.5
LHA Aries	285°	285°	286°
Hc	26°37'	51°19'	17°04'
Zn	**271°**	**160°**	**034°**
SA	26°32'.0	51°19'.4	17°08'.7
IE and dip	-3'.6	-3'.6	-3'.6
AA	26°28'.4	51°15'.8	17°05'.1
Corrn	-1'.9	-0'.8	-3'.1
TA	26°26'.5	51°15'.0	17°02'.0
CA	26°37'.0	51°19'.0	17°04'.0
Intercept	**10'.5** A	**4'.0** A	**2'.0** A

Chosen latitude 46° N

Chosen longitudes	**7°50'.5W**	**7°58'.7W**	**7°19'.5W**

5.4

	h m
Dawn twilight	04 48 LMT 8d
Long W as time	+10 40
	15 28 GMT 8d

	Suhail	Aldebaran	Achernar	Sirius
GMT	15h 28m 00s	15h 28m 40s	15h 29m 12s	15h 29m 59s
GHA Aries 15h	241°40'.6	241°40'.6	241°40'.6	241°40'.6
Incre	+7°01'.1	+7°11'.2	+7°19'.2	+7°31'.0
GHA Aries	248°41'.7	248°51'.8	248°59'.8	249°11'.6
C long W	-159°41'.7	-159°51'.8	-159°59'.8	-160°11'.6
LHA Aries	89°	89°	89°	89°
Hc	56°23'	24°54'	49°58'	59°00'
Zn	**103°**	**339°**	**229°**	**023°**
SA	56°17'.7	24°48'.5	50°04'.6	58°56'.9
IE and dip	-1'.3	-1'.3	-1'.3	-1'.3
AA	56°16'.4	24°47'.2	50°03'.3	58°55'.6
Corrn	-0'.6	-2'.1	-0'.8	-0'.6
TA	56°15'.8	24°45'.1	50°02'.5	58°55'.0
CA	56°23'.0	24°54'.0	49°58'.0	59°00'.0
Intercept	**7'.2** A	**8'.9** A	**4'.5** T	**5'.0** A

5.5

	h m
Dawn twilight	04 48 LMT 8d
Long E as time	-06 07
	22 41 GMT 7d

GHA Aries 22h	345°58'.7
Incre 41m	+10°16'.7
GHA Aries	356°15'.4
DR long E	+91°45'.1
	448°00'.5
-360°	-360°00'.0
LHA Aries	88°00'.5 (use 88°)

(a) **Stars available:**

	Hc	Zn
BETELGEUSE	**36°36'**	**001°**
SIRIUS	**58°43'**	**025°**
◇ **Suhail**	**55°43'**	**104°**
RIGIL KENT	**23°44'**	**157°**
◇ **ACHERNAR**	**50°30'**	**230°**
Diphda	**21°37'**	**266°**
◇ **ALDEBARAN**	**25°09**	**340°**

(b) **Suhail, Achernar, Aldebaran.**

(c) The choice may be made **using pairs of stars which give a cut as near right angles as possible** such as Betelgeuse and Diphda (95°), Rigil Kent and Achernar (77°).

5.6

	h m
Dawn twilight	03 30 LMT 14d
Long W as time	+11 11
	14 41 GMT 14d
GHA Aries 14h	112°18'.0
Incre 41m	+10°16'.7
GHA Aries	122°34'.7
+360°	+360°
	482°34'.7
DR long W	-167°45'.0
LHA Aries	**314°49'.7** (use 315°)

(a) **Stars available:**

	Hc	Zn
CAPELLA	**14°22'**	**037°**
◇ **Hamal**	**25°42'**	**082°**
Alpheratz	**49°49'**	**098°**
Enif	**52°38'**	**162°**
◇ **ALTAIR**	**49°55'**	**207°** (Star 2)
VEGA	**62°46'**	**268°** (Star 3)
◇ **Kochab**	**43°12'**	**338°** (Star 1)

(b)

	Kochab	Altair	Vega
GMT	14h 40m 01s	14h 40m 50s	14h 41m 59s
GHA Aries 14h	112°18'.0	112°18'.0	112°18'.0
Incre	10°01'.9	10°14'.2	+10°31'.5
GHA Aries	122°19'.9	122°32'.2	122°49'.5
+360°	+360°	+360°	+360°
	482°19'.9	482°32'.2	482°49'.5
C long W	-167°19'.9	-167°32'.2	-167°49'.5
LHA Aries	315°	315°	315°
Hc	43°12'	49°55'	62°46'
Zn	**338°**	**207°**	**268°**
SA	43°11'.1	50°01'.0	62°37'.1
IE and dip	-0'.1	-0'.1	-0'.1
AA	43°11'.0	50°00'.9	62°37'.0
Corrn	-1'.0	-0'.8	-0'.5
TA	43°10'.0	50°00'.1	62°36'.5
CA	43°12'.0	49°55'.0	62°46'.0
Intercept	**2'.0** A	**5'.1** T	**9'.5** A

5.7

	h m
Dusk twilight	20 31 LMT 13d
Long W as time	+11 10
	07 41 GMT 14d

	Star 1 Arcturus	Star 2 Vega	Star 3 Dubhe
GMT	07h 40m 00s	07h 40m 25s	07h 41m 48s
GHA Aries 07h	7°00'.7	7°00'.7	7°00'.7
Incre	+10°01'.6	+10°07'.9	+10°28'.7
GHA Aries	17°02'.3	17°08'.6	17°29'.4
+360°	+360°	+360°	+360°
	377°02'.3	377°08'.6	377°29'.4
C long W	-167°02'.3	-167°08'.6	-167°29'.4
LHA Aries	210°	210°	210°
Hc	63°05'	40°04'	60°19'
Zn	**172°**	**072°**	**318°**
SA	63°04'.0	39°59'.6	60°25'.6
IE and dip	-4'.5	-4'.5	-4'.5
AA	62°59'.5	39°55'.1	60°21'.1
Corrn	-0'.5	-1'.2	-0'.6
TA	62°59'.0	39°53'.9	60°20'.5
CA	63°05'.0	40°04'.0	60°19'.0
Intercept	**6'.0** A	**10'.1** A	**1'.5** T

5.8

	h m
Dawn twilight	03 30 LMT 14d
Long E as time	-10 36
	16 54 GMT 13d

	Enif	Alphecca	Rasalhague	Altair
GMT	16h 54m 01s	16h 54m 30s	16h 55m 05s	16h 55m 59s
GHA Aries 16h	141°23'.8	141°23'.8	141°23'.8	141°23'.8
Incre	+13°32'.5	+13°39'.7	+13°48'.5	+14°02'.0
GHA Aries	154°56'.3	155°03'.5	155°12'.3	155°25'.8
C long E	+159°03'.7	+158°56'.5	+158°47'.7	+159°34'.2
LHA Aries	314°	314°	314°	315°
Hc	52°25'	25°15'	36°02'	49°55'
Zn	**161°**	**283°**	**249°**	**207°**
SA	52°37'.0	25°10'.8	35°53'.8	50°11'.3
IE and dip	-4'.5	-4'.5	-4'.5	-4'.5
AA	52°32'.5	25°06'.3	35°49'.3	50°06'.8
Corrn	-0'.7	-2'.1	-1'.3	-0'.8
TA	52°31'.8	25°04'.2	35°48'.0	50°06'.0
CA	52°25'.0	25°15'.0	36°02'.0	49°55'.0
Intercept	**6'.8** T	**10'.8** A	**14'.0** A	**11'.0** T

5.9

	h m	
Dusk twilight	20 30 LMT 14d	
Long E as time	-10 35	
	09 55 GMT 14d	
GHA Aries 09h	37°05'.7	
Incre 55m	-13°47'.3	
GHA Aries	50°53'.0	
DR long E	+158°45'.0	
LHA Aries	209°38'.0 (use 210°)	

Stars available:

	Hc	Zn
DENEB	**25°04'**	**050°**
◇ **VEGA**	**40°04'**	**072°**
Rasalhague	**34°00'**	**109°**
◇ **ARCTURUS**	**63°05'**	**172°**
Denebola	**48°15'**	**232°**
REGULUS	**30°36'**	**255°**
◇ **Dubhe**	**60°19'**	**318°**

5.10

	h m
Dawn twilight	04 48 LMT 8d
Long E as time	-05 31
	23 17 GMT 7d

	Suhail	Aldebaran	Achernar
GMT	23h 16m 03s	23h 17m 25s	23h 17m 51s
GHA Aries 16h	1°01'.1	1°01'.1	1°01'.1
Incre	+4°01'.4	+4°22'.0	+4°28'.5
GHA Aries	5°02'.5	5°23'.1	5°29'.6
C long E	+82°57'.5	+82°36'.9	+82°30'.4
LHA Aries	88°	88°	88°
Hc	55°43'	25°09'	50°30'
Zn	**104°**	**340°**	**230°**
SA	55°34'.1	25°04'.5	50°34'.3
IE and dip	-1'.4	-1'.4	-1'.4
AA	55°32'.7	25°03'.1	50°32'.9
Corrn	-0'.7	-2'.1	-0'.8
TA	55°32'.0	25°01'.0	50°32'.1
CA	55°43'.0	25°09'.0	50°30'.0
Intercept	11'.0 A	8'.0 A	2'.1 T

CHAPTER 6

6.1

	h m
Dusk twilight	20 32 LMT 13d
Long W as time	+10
	20 42 GMT 13d

		Alphecca		Rasalhague		Denebola
SHA star		126°30'.1		96°27'.4		182°57'.0
GHA Aries 20h		+201°33'.6		+201°33'.6		+201°33'.6
Incre		+10°01'.9		+10°14'.7		+10°23'.2
GHA star		338°05'.6		308°15'.7		394°53'.8
C long W		-2°05'.6		-2°15'.7		-2°53'.8
						392°
						-360°
LHA star		336°		306°		32°
Dec		N26°46'.3		N12°34'.3		N14°40'.1
Hc		62°20'		33°18'		48°13'
d	+48	+37	+44	+25	+50	+33
CA		**62°57'**		**33°43'**		**48°46'**
Z		128°		109°		130°
Zn		**128°**		**109°**		**230°** (360°-Z)

6.2

	h m
Dawn twilight	04 48 LMT 7d
Long W as time	+6 06
	10 54 GMT 7d

		Rigel		Menkar		Alphard
SHA star		281°33'.8		314°38'.6		218°18'.6
GHA Aries 10h		+165°29'.1		+165°29'.1		+165°29'.1
Incre		+13°42'.0		+13°49'.5		+13°53'.3
GHA star		460°44'.9		493°57'.2		397°41'.0
C long W		-91°44'.9		-91°57'.2		-91°41'.0
		369°		402°		
-360°		-360°		-360°		
LHA star		9°		42°		306°
Dec		S8°13'.0		N4°01'.7		S8°35'.0
Hc		51°13'		27°42'		30°18'
d	+59	+13	-51	-2	+45	+26
CA		51°26'		27°40'		30°44'
Z		166°		131°		112°
Zn		**346°** (180°+Z)		**311°** (180°+Z)		**068°** (180°-Z)
SA		51°14'.7		27°21'.3		30°48'.5
IE and dip		-0'.4		-0'.4		-0'.4
AA		51°14'.3		27°20'.9		30°48'.1
Corrn		-0'.8		-1'.9		-1'.6
TA		51°13'.5		27°19'.0		30°46'.5
CA		51°26'.0		27°40'.0		30°44'.0
Intercept		**12'.5** A		**21'.0** A		**2'.5** T

6.3

		h m
Dawn twilight		03 30 LMT 13d
Long W as time		+58
		04 28 GMT 13d

	Rasalhague	Altair	Alphecca
SHA star	96°27'.4	62°30'.3	126°30'.1
GHA Aries 04h	+320°54'.2	+320°54'.2	+320°54'.2
Incre	+7°05'.9	+7°15'.7	+7°20'.0
GHA star	424°27'.5	390°40'.2	454°44'.3
C long W	**-14°27'.5**	**-14°40'.2**	**-14°44'.3**
	410°	376°	440°
-360°	-360°	-360°	-360°
LHA star	50°	16°	80°
Dec	N12°34'.3	N8°49'.3	N26°46'.3
Hc	35°54'	49°35'	25°04'
d	+45 +26	+57 +47	+40 +31
CA	36°20'	50°22'	25°35'
Z	112°	155°	78°
Zn	**248**° (360°-Z)	**205**° (360°-Z)	**282**° (360°-Z)
SA	36°15'.3	50°13'.5	25°22'.4
IE and dip	-1'.1	-1'.1	-1'.1
AA	36°14'.2	50°12'.4	25°21'.3
Corrn	-1'.3	-0'.8	-2'.0
TA	36°12'.9	50°11'.6	25°19'.3
CA	36°20'.0	50°22'.0	25°35'.0
Intercept	**7'.1** A	**10'.4** A	**15'.7** A

6.4

	h m
Dawn twilight	05 36 LMT 7d
Long W as time	+50
	06 26 GMT 7d

		Rigel		Procyon		Regulus
SHA star		281°33'.8		245°23'.5		208°07'.9
GHA Aries 06h		+105°19'.2		+105°19'.2		+105°19'.2
Incre		+7°04'.7		+7°13'.9		+7°19'.2
GHA star		393°57'.7		357°56'.6		320°46'.3
C long W		**-12°57'.7**		**-12°56'.6**		**-12°46'.3**
		381°				
-360°		-360°				
LHA star		21°		345°		308°
Dec		S8°13'.0		N5°16'.2		N12°03'.0
Hc		32°50'		46°59'		34°36'
d	-58	-13	+58	+15	+45	+02
CA		32°37'		47°14'		34°38'
Z		155°		158°		111°
Zn		**205°** (360°-Z)		**158°**		**111°**
SA		32°39'.6		47°33'.4		34°56'.4
IE and dip		-0'.1		-0'.1		-0'.1
AA		33°39'.5		47°33'.3		34°56'.3
Corrn		-1'.5		-0'.9		-1'.4
TA		32°38'.0		47°32'.4		34°54'.9
CA		32°37'.0		47°14'.0		34°38'.0
Intercept		**1'.0** T		**18'.4** T		**16'.9** T

6.5

	h m		
Dusk twilight	18 47 LMT **8d**		
Long W as time	+6 41		
	01 28 GMT 9d		
	Enif	Sabik	Zubenelgenubi
SHA star	34°09'.2	102°38'.8	137°30'.9
GHA Aries 01h	+32°05'.2	+32°05'.2	+32°05'.2
Incre	7°01'.7	7°12'.9	7°19'.2
GHA star	73°16'.1	141°56'.9	176°55'.3
+360°	+360°		
	433°16'.1		
C long W	-100°16'.1	-99°56'.9	-99°55'.3
LHA star	333°	42°	77°
Dec	N9°48'.1	S15°42'.3	S15°58'.3
Hc	29°55'	43°13'	19°42'
d	-56 -45	+46 +32	+42 +41
CA	29°10'	43°45'	20°23'
Z	149°	118°	89°
Zn	**031°** (180°-Z)	**298°** (180°+Z)	**269°** (180°+Z)
SA	29°10'.5	44°06'.4	20°47'.5
IE and dip	-1'.1	-1'.1	-1'.1
AA	29°09'.4	44°05'.3	20°46'.4
Corrn	-1'.7	-1'.0	-2'.5
TA	29°07'.7	44°04'.3	20°43'.9
CA	29°10'.0	43°45'.0	20°23'.0
Intercept	**2'.3** A	**19'.3** T	**20'.9** T

6.6

	h m
Dusk twilight	20 30 LMT 12d
Long W as time	+1 11
	21 41 GMT 12d

	Spica	Pollux	Arcturus
SHA star	158°55'.3	243°56'.1	146°16'.4
GHA Aries 21h	+215°37'.0	+215°37'.0	+215°37'.0
Incre	+10°02'.1	+10°10'.9	+10°19'.4
GHA star	384°34'.4	469°44'.0	372°12'.8
C long W	**-17°34'.4**	**-17°44'.0**	**-18°12'.8**
	367°	452°	354°
-360°	-360°	-360°	
LHA star	7°	92°	354°
Dec	S11°04'.5	N28°04'.2	N19°16'.2
Hc	32°39'	18°26'	62°33'
d	-59 -05	+41 +03	+59 +16
CA	32°34'	18°29'	62°49'
Z	172°	69°	168°
Zn	**188°** (360°-Z)	**291°** (360°-Z)	**168°**
SA	32°47'.3	18°32'.5	63°02'.1
IE and dip	+0'.4	+0'.4	+0'.4
AA	32°47'.7	18°32'.9	63°02'.5
Corrn	-1'.5	-2'.9	-0'.5
TA	32°46'.2	18°30'.0	63°02'.0
CA	32°34'.0	18°29'.0	62°49'.0
Intercept	**12'.2** T	**1'.0** T	**13'.0** T

6.7

	h m
Dusk twilight	20 33 LMT 12d
Long W as time	+1 22
	21 55 GMT 12d

	Alphecca	Rasalhague	Regulus
SHA star	126°30'.1	96°27'.4	208°08'.0
GHA Aries 21h	+215°37'.0	+215°37'.0	+215°37'.0
Incre	+13°42'.5	+13°46'.5	+13°52'.5
GHA star	355°49'.6	325°50'.9	437°37'.5
C long W	**-20°49'.6**	**-20°50'.9**	**-20°37'.5**
			417°
-360°			-360°
LHA star	335°	305°	57°
Dec	N26°46'.3	N12°34'.3	N12°03'.1
Hc	61°47'	32°38'	31°18'
d	+47 +36	+44 +25	+44 +02
CA	62°23'	33°03'	31°20'
Z	127°	108°	106°
Zn	**127°**	**108°**	**254°** (360°-Z)
SA	62°28'.8	33°19'.4	31°05'.4
IE and dip	-0'.3	-0'.3	-0'.3
AA	62°28'.5	33°19'.1	31°05'.1
Corrn	-0'.5	-1'.5	-1'.6
TA	62°28'.0	33°17'.6	31°03'.5
CA	62°23'.0	33°03'.0	31°20'.0
Intercept	**5'.0** T	**14'.6** T	**16'.5** A

6.8

	h m
Dawn twilight	04 48 LMT 8d
Long W as time	+10 40
	15 28 GMT 8d

	Diphda	Betelgeuse
SHA star	349°18'.3	271°25'.8
GHA Aries 15h	+241°40'.6	+241°40'.6
Incre	+7°02'.9	+7°18'.7
GHA star	598°01'.8	520°25'.1
C long W	-160°01'.8	-160°25'.1
	438°	360°
-360°	-360°	-360°
LHA star	78°	000°
Dec	S18°04'.5	N7°24'.4
Z	86°	180°
Zn	266° (180°+Z)	000° (180°-Z)

The position lines of these two stars give a good angle of cut.

6.9

	h m		
Dusk twilight	20 33 LMT 14d		
Long W as time	+1 43		
	22 16 GMT 14d		
	Denebola	Arcturus	Alphecca
SHA star	182°57'.0	146°16'.4	126°30'.1
GHA Aries 22h	+232°37'.7	+232°37'.7	+232°37'.7
Incre	+4°01'.4	+4°09'.9	+4°20'.2
GHA star	419°36'.1	383°04'.0	363°28'.0
C long W	**-25°36'.1**	**-26°04'.0**	**-25°28'.0**
	394°		
-360°	-360°		
LHA star	34°	357°	338°
Dec	N14°40'.1	N19°16'.2	N26°46'.3
Hc	47°07'	62°53'	63°25'
d	+50 +33	+60 +16	+48 +37
CA	47°40'	63°09'	64°02'
Z	127°	174°	131°
Zn	**233°** (360°-Z)	**174°**	**131°**
SA	47°32'.9	62°47'.9	63°40'.1
IE and dip	-3'.5	-3'.5	-3'.5
AA	47°29'.4	62°44'.4	63°36'.6
Corrn	-0'.9	-0'.5	-0'.5
TA	47°28'.5	62°43'.9	63°36'.1
CA	47°40'.0	63°09'.0	64°02'.0
Intercept	**11'.5** A	**25'.1** A	**25'.9** A

6.10

		h m	
Dawn twilight		04 49 LMT 9d	
Long E as time		-10 20	
		18 29 GMT 8d	

		Bellatrix		Procyon		Alphard
SHA star		278°56'.3		245°23'.5		218°18'.6
GHA Aries 18h		+286°47'.9		+286°47'.9		+286°47'.9
Incre		+7°02'.4		+7°13'.7		+7°24'.0
GHA star		572°46'.6		539°25'.1		512°30'.5
C long E		**+155°13'.4**		**+154°34'.9**		**+154°29'.5**
		728°		694°		667°
	-720°	-720°	-360°	360°	-360°	-360°
LHA star		8°		334°		307°
C lat 46° S						
Dec		N6°20'.3		N5°16'.2		S8°35'.0
Hc		37°31'		34°00'		30°56'
d	-60	-20	-55	-15	+46	+27
CA		37°11'		33°45'		31°23'
Z		170°		148°		113°
Zn		**350°** (180°+Z)		**032°** (180°-Z)		**067°** (180°-Z)
SA		37°33'.7		34°01'.1		31°18'.0
IE and dip		-1'.4		-1'.4		-1'.4
AA		37°32'.3		33°59'.7		31°16'.6
Corrn		-1'.3		-1'.4		-1'.6
TA		37°31'.0		33°58'.3		31°15'.0
CA		37°11'.0		33°45'.0		31°23'.0
Intercept		**20'.0** T		**13'.3** T		**8'.0** A

CHAPTER 7

7.1

	h m
Dusk twilight	18 47 LMT 7d
Long W as time	+2 41
	21 28 GMT 7d

GHA Jupiter 21h	84°48'.6	DEC	S21°08'.6
Incre 29m 12s	+7°18'.0	d 0.1	0'.0
v 2.0	+1'.0		S21°08'.6
GHA Jupiter	92°07'.6		
C long W	-40°07'.6		
LHA Jupiter	52°		

Hc		41°05'	SA	41°25'.4
d	+41	+6	IE and dip	-3'.8
		41°11'	AA	41°21'.6
			Corrn	-1'.1
Z		103°	TA	41°20'.5
Zn		**283°** (180°+Z)	CA	41°11'.0
			Intercept	**9'.5** T

7.2

	h m		
Dawn twilight	04 48 LMT 8d		
Long W as time	+10 40		
	15 28 GMT		
GHA Venus 15h	88°53'.2	DEC	N8°11'.0
Incre 28m 17s	+7°04'.3	d 0.2	-0'.1
v 0.7	+0'.3		N8°10'.9
GHA Venus	95°57'.8		
+360	+360°		
	455°57'.8		
C long W	**-159°57'.8**		
LHA Venus	296°00'.0		

Hc	11°37'	SA	11°21'.0
d -46	-8	IE and dip	+0'.4
		AA	11°21'.4
CA	11°29'	Corrn	-4'.7
			11°16'.7
Z	115°	Add corrn	+0'.3
Zn	**065°** (180°-Z)	TA	11°17'.0
		CA	11°29'.0
		Intercept	**12'.0** A

7.3

	h m		
Dusk twilight	20 29 LMT 14d		
Long W as time	+9		
	20 38 GMT 14d		
GHA Saturn 20h	355°38'.7	DEC	S8°18'.0
Incre 29m 59s	+7°29'.8	d 0.0	
v 2.5	+1'.2		
GHA Saturn	363°09'.7		
-360°	-360°		
	3°09'.7		
C long W	**-2°09'.7**		
LHA Saturn	1°		

Chosen position 46° N 2°09'.7W.

Hc	36°00'	SA	35°56'.0
d -60	-18	IE and dip	-3'.8
	35°42'	AA	35°52'.2
		Corrn	-1'.3
Z	179°	TA	35°50'.9
Zn	**181°** (360°-Z)	CA	35°42'.0
		Intercept	**8'.9** T

7.4

	h m		
Dawn twilight	05 36 LMT 7d		
Long W as time	+1 18		
	06 54 GMT 7d		
GHA Mars 06h	308°28'.6	DEC	N11°05'.4
Incre 55m 10s	+13°47'.5	d 0.6	-0'.6
v 1.0	+0'.9		N11°04'.8
GHA Mars	322°17'.0		
C long W	-19°17'.0		
LHA Mars	303°		

Hc		30°34'	SA	30°56'.9
d	+44	+4'	IE and dip	-0'.5
CA		30°38'	AA	30°56'.4
			Corrn	-1'.6
				30°54'.8
Z		107°	Add corrn	+0'.1
Zn		**107°**	TA	30°54'.9
			CA	30°38'.0
			Intercept	**16'.9** T

7.5

	h m		
Dusk twilight	20 31 LMT 12d		
Long W as time	+11 11		
	07 42 GMT 13d		
GHA Venus 07h	235°59'.9	DEC	N20°38'.2
Incre 41m 59s	+10°29'.8	d 0.7	-0'.5
v 0.0	0'.0		N20°37'.7
GHA Venus	246°29'.7		
C long W	-167°29'.7		
LHA Venus	79°		

Hc		21°45'	SA	22°21'.3
d	+41	+26	IE and dip	-4'.9
CA		22°11	AA	22°16'.4
			Corrn	-2'.4
				22°14'.0
Z		83°	Add corrn	+0'.2
Zn		**277°**(360°-Z)	TA	22°14'.2
			CA	22°11'.0
			Intercept	**3'.2** T

7.6

	h m		
Dawn twilight	04 48 LMT 8d		
Long E as time	-6 07		
	22 41 GMT 7d		
GHA Venus 22h	193°40'.3	DEC	N8°14'.7
Incre 41m 58s	+10°29'.5	d 0.2	-0'.1
v 0.7	+0'.5		N8°14'.6
GHA Venus	204°10'.3		
C long E	**+91°49'.7**		
LHA Venus	296°		

Chosen position 46°S 91°49'.7E.

Hc 11°37'		SA	11°48'.5
d -46 -12		IE and dip	-4'.2
CA 11°25		AA	11°44'.3
		Corrn	-4'.6
			11°39'.7
Z 115°		Add corrn	+0'.3
Zn **065°**(180°-Z)		TA	11°40'.0
		CA	11°25'.0
		Intercept	**15'.0** T

7.7

	h m		
Dawn twilight	04 48 LMT 8d		
Long E as time	-5 31		
	23 17 GMT 7d		
GHA Venus 23h	208°41'.1	DEC	N8°14'.5
Incre 17h 57m	+4°29'.3	d 0.2	-0'.1
v 0.7	+0'.2		N8°14'.4
GHA Venus	213°10'.6		
C long E	+82°49'.4		
LHA Venus	296°		

Hc 11°37'		SA	11°36'.3
d -46 -11'		IE and dip	-4'.5
CA 11°26		AA	11°31'.8
		Corrn	-4'.6
			11°27'.2
Z 115°		Add corrn	+0'.3
Zn **065°**(180°-Z)		TA	11°27'.5
		CA	11°26'.0
		Intercept	**1'.5** T

7.8

	h m		
Dusk twilight	20 28 LMT 14d		
Long E as time	-11 00		
	09 28 GMT 14d		
GHA Saturn 09h	190°10'.9	DEC	S8°18'.1
Incre 29m 10s	+7°17'.5	d 0.0	
v 2.5	+1'.2		
GHA Saturn	197°29'.6		
C long E	-164°30'.4		
	362°		
-360°	-360°		
LHA Saturn	2°		

Hc		35°58'	SA	36°04'.4
d	-60	-18'	IE and dip	-4'.4
			AA	36°00'.0
CA		35°40'	Corrn	-1'.3
			TA	35°58'.7
Z		178°	CA	35°40'.0
Zn		**182°** (360°-Z)		
			Intercept	**18'.7** T

7.9

	h m		
Dusk twilight	18 47 LMT 8d		
Long E as time	-10 07		
	08 40 GMT 8d		
GHA Jupiter 08h	250°10'.7	DEC	S21°09'.5
Incre 41m 50s	+10°27'.5	(No d correction necessary as declination remains the same for 09h.)	
v 2.0	+1'.4		
GHA Jupiter	260°39'.6		
C long E	+151°20'.4		
	412°		
-360°	-360°		
LHA Jupiter	52°		

Hc		41°05'	SA	41°05'.2
d	+41	+7'	IE and dip	+0'.1
			AA	41°05'.3
		41°12'	Corrn	-1'.1
			TA	41°04'.2
Z		103°	CA	41°12'.0
Zn		**283°** (180°+Z)		
			Intercept	**7'.8** A

7.10

	h m		
Dawn twilight	05 36 LMT 7d		
Long W as time	+41		
	06 17 GMT 7d		
GHA Mars 06h	308°28'.6	DEC	N11°05'.4
Incre 16m 50s	+4°12'.5	d 0.6	-0'.2
v +1.0	+0'.3		
GHA Mars	312°41'.4		N11°05'.2
C long W	-10°41'.4		
LHA Mars	302°		

Hc		29°55	SA	30°22'.2
d	+43	+4	IE and dip	-1'.8
			AA	30°20'.4
CA		29°59	Corrn	-1'.7
				30°18'.7
Z		106°	Add corrn	+0'.1
Zn		**106°**	TA	30°18'.8
			CA	29°59'.0
			Intercept	**19'.8** T

CHAPTER 8

8.1

	h m
MP Sun	12 00 LMT 12d at DR
Long W as time	+28
	12 28 GMT 12d at DR

8.2

DEC	N23°07'.8	SA	33°01'.4
d 0.1	0'.0	IE and dip	-2'.0
	N23°07'.8	AA	32°59'.4
		Corrn UL	-17'.3
		TA	32°42'.1
			90°00'.0
		TA	-32°42'.1
		TZD	57°17'.9
		DEC	-23°07'.8
		Latitude	**34°10'.1S**

8.3

DEC	S19°43'.3	SA	46°42'.1
d 0.6	-0'.2	IE and dip	+0'.3
	S19°43'.1	AA	46°42'.4
		Corrn LL	+15'.3
		TA	46°57'.7
			90°00'.0
		TA	-46°57'.7
		TZD	43°02'.3
		DEC	-19°43'.1
		Latitude	**23°19'.2N**

8.4 (a)

	h m	
MP Sun	12 12	LMT 24d at DR
Long E as time	-5 18	
	06 54	**GMT 24d at DR**

(b)

DEC	S19°20'.0	SA	68°27'.4
d 0.6	-0'.5	IE and dip	-2'.1
	S19°19'.5	AA	68°25'.3
		Corrn UL	-16'.5
		TA	68°08'.8
			90°00'.0
		TA	-68°08'.8
		TZD	21°51'.2
		DEC	+19°19'.5
		Latitude	**41°10'.7S**

8.5

	h m s	
	11 28 15	ZT 7d
Zone -11	-11	
	00 28 15	GMT 7d

DEC	S5°11'.7	SA	50°19'.8
d 1.0	+0'.5	IE and dip	-3'.4
	S5°12'.2	AA	50°16'.4
		Corrn UL	-16'.9
		TA	49°59'.5
			90°00'.0
		TA	-49°59'.5
		TZD	40°00'.5
		DEC	+5°12'.2
		Latitude	**45°12'.7S**

8.6

GHA Sun 15h	45°01'.4	DEC	N23°12'.1
Incre 16m 51s	+4°12'.8	d 0.1	0'.0
GHA Sun	49°14'.2		N23°12'.1
C long W	-4°14'.2		
LHA Sun	45°		

Hc		47°09'	SA	47°27'.4
d	+42	+8	IE and dip	-3'.8
			AA	47°23'.6
CA		47°17'	Corrn UL	-16'.7
Z	107°		TA	47°06'.9
Zn	**253°** (360°-Z)		CA	47°17'.0
			Intercept	**10'.1** A

Using NP 401 Sight Reduction Tables for Marine Navigation:

Chosen Lat		46°N		
DEC		23°12'.1N		
LHA		45°		
Hc		47°09'.4	Z	106°6 (after interpolation)
d	+41.2	+8'.0 (40)	**Zn**	**253°4** (360°-Z)
		+0'.2 (1.2)		
CA		47°17'.6		
TA		47°06'.9		
Intercept		**10'.7** A		

Using the Haversine Formula to find Hc (*Norie's Nautical Tables*):

LHA	45°21'.2	9.17212 LH
DR lat	45°37'.0N	+9.84476 LC
DEC	23°12'.1N	+9.96337 LC
		8.98025 LH
Lat ~ DEC	22°24'.9	0.09555 NH
		+0.03778 NH
CZD	42°50'.0	
From 90°	90°	0.13333 NH
CA	47°10'.0	
TA	47°06'.9	
Intercept	**3'.1** A	

Using ABC tables to find Zn (*Norie's Nautical Tables*):

A = 1.00S (LHA and lat)
B = -0.61N

C = 0.39S

0.39S = S74°7W = **254°.7**

8.7

	h m s			
	08 55 21 ZT 23d			
Zone +11	+11			
	19 55 21 GMT 23d			
GHA Sun 19h	102°02'.0		DEC	S19°26'.5
Incre 55m 21s	+13°50'.3		d 0.6	-0'.6
GHA Sun	115°52'.3			S19°25'.9
+360°	+360°			
	475°52'.3			
C long W	-160°52'.3			
LHA Sun	315°			

Hc		44°19'	SA	44°42'.1
d	+43	+19'	IE and dip	-3'.5
CA		44°38'	AA	44°38'.6
			Corrn LL	+15'.3
Z		111°	TA	44°53'.9
Zn		**069°** (180°-Z)	CA	44°38'.0
			Intercept	**15'.9** T

8.8

```
                          h  m  s
                         09 29 10 ZT   12d
Zone +8                  +8
                         17 29 10 GMT 12d

GHA Sun 17h                     75°04'.2      DEC          N23°08'.8
Incre 29m 10s                    7°17'.5      d  0.1           0'.0
GHA Sun                         82°21'.7                   N23°08'.8
+360°                         +360°
                               442°21'.7
C long W                      -120°21'.7
LHA Sun                        322°

Hc        51°43'                          SA               52°02'.2
d    +43      +6                          IE and dip          -5'.2
CA        51°49'                          AA               51°57'.0
                                          Corrn LL           +15'.2
Z        114°                             TA               52°12'.2
Zn       114°                             CA               51°49'.0
                                          Intercept           23'.2 T
```

8.9

```
                           h  m  s
                          16 40 31 ZT   24d
Zone -10                 -10
                          06 40 31 GMT 24d

GHA Sun 06h                    267°00'.3      DEC          S19°20'.0
Incre 40m 31s                 +10°07'.8       d  0.6          -0'.4
GHA Sun                        277°08'.1                   S19°19'.6
C long E                      +154°51'.9
                               432°
-360°                          360°
LHA Sun                         72°

Hc        25°55                           SA               26°27'.1
d    +41    +14                           IE and dip          -2'.0
CA        26°09'                          AA               26°25'.1
                                          Corrn UL           -18'.0
Z         89°                             TA               26°07'.1
Zn       269°(180° +Z)                    CA               26°09'.0
                                          Intercept            1'.9 A
```

8.10

	h m s	
	14 16 23	ZT 8d
Zone +10	+10	
	00 16 23	GMT 9d

GHA Sun 00h	183°06'.9	DEC	S5°57'.6
Incre 16m 23s	+4°05'.8	d 1.0	+0'.3
GHA Sun	187°12'.7		S5°57'.9
C long W	-151°12'.7		
LHA	36°		

Hc		38°30'	SA	39°53'.2
d	+51	+49	IE and dip	-5'.6
CA		39°19'	AA	39°47'.6
			Corrn UL	-17'.2
Z		132°	TA	39°30'.4
Zn		**312°(180°+Z)**	CA	39°19'.0
			Intercept	**11'.4** T

CHAPTER 9

9.1

	h m	
Meridian passage	20 10	LMT 24d at GM
Meridian passage	-19 15	LMT 23d at GM
Daily difference	55	

$\frac{10.42}{360} \times 55 = 1.59$m (use 2m)

(10.42 is the decimal equivalent of 10°25'.4)

	h m	
Meridian passage	19 15	LMT 23d at GM
Long W corrn	+2	
	19 17	LMT 23d at DR
Long W as time	+42	
	19 59	**GMT 23d at DR**

9.2

	h m	
Meridian passage	20 10	LMT 24d at GM
Meridian passage	-19 15	LMT 23d at GM
Daily difference	55	

$\frac{80.3}{360} \times 55 = 12.26$m (use 12m)

	h m	
Meridian passage	20 10	LMT 24d at GM
Long E corrn	-12	
	19 58	LMT 24d at DR
Long E as time	-5 21	
	14 37	**GMT 24d at DR**

9.3

	h m	
Meridian passage	19 15	LMT 23d at GM
Meridian passage	-18 25	LMT 22d at GM
Daily difference	50	

$\frac{27}{360} \times 50 = 3.75\text{m}$ (use 4m)

	h m	
Meridian passage	18 25	LMT 22d at GM
Long W corrn	+4	
	18 29	LMT 22d at DR
Long W as time	+1 48	
	20 17	GMT 22d at DR

DEC	N10°39'.2		90°00'.0
d +12.1	+3'.5	TA	-75°54'.2
	N10°42'.7	TZD	14°05'.8
		DEC	+10°42'.7
		Latitude	**24°48'.5N**

9.4 (a)

	h m	
Meridian passage	19 15	LMT 23d at GM
Meridian passage	-18 25	LMT 22d at GM
Daily difference	50	

$\frac{167.75}{360} \times 50 = 23.3\text{m}$ (use 23m)

	h m	
Meridian passage	19 15	LMT 23d at GM
Long E corrn	-23	
	18 52	LMT 23d at DR
Long E as time	-11 11	
	07 41	GMT 23d at DR
Zone -11	+11	
	18 41	**ZT 23d at DR**

(b)

DEC	N12°50'.0		90°00'.0
d 11.6	+8'.0	TA	-82°19'.2
	N12°58'.0	TZD	7°40'.8
		DEC	12°58'.0
		TZD	-7°40'.8
		Latitude	**5°17'.2N**

9.5

	h m	
Meridian passage	20 10	LMT 24d at GM
Meridian passage	19 15	LMT 23d at GM
Daily difference	55	

$\frac{35}{360} \times 55 = 5.3$m (use 5m)

	h m	
Meridian passage	19 15	LMT 23d at GM
Long W corrn	+5	
	19 20	LMT 23d at DR
Long W as time	+2 20	
	21 40	GMT 23d at DR

DEC	N15°27'.0	HP 58.6
d 10.7	+7'.2	
	N15°34'.2	

SA	34°34'.1
IE and dip	-0'.9
AA	34°33'.2
Corrn	+56'.8
HP UL	+4'.1
	35°34'.1
-30'	-30'.0
TA	35°04'.1
	90°00'.0
TA	-35°04'.1
TZD	54°55'.9
DEC	-15°34'.2
Latitude	**39°21'.7S**

9.6

	h m s	
	20 40 07	ZT 14d
Zone -11	-11	
	09 40 07	GMT 14d

GHA Moon 09h	267°13'.6
Incre 40m 07s	+9°34'.3
v 4.5	+3'.0
GHA Moon	276°50'.9
C long E	+159°09'.1
	436°
-360°	-360°
	76°

DEC	N22°02'.0
d 7.0	-4'.7
	N21°57'.3
HP 60.3	

Hc		24°30'
d	+40	+38
CA		25°08'
Z		85°
Zn		**275°** (360°-Z)

SA	23°49'.9
IE and dip	+0'.2
AA	23°50'.1
Corrn	+61'.2
HP LL	+8'.1
TA	24°59'.4
CA	25°08'.0
Intercept	**8'.6** A

9.7

	h m		
Dusk twilight	20 33 LMT 13d		
Long W as time	+11 09		
	07 42 GMT 14d		
GHA Moon 07h	238°26'.8	DEC	N22°15'.5
Incre 41m 38s	+9°56'.1	d 6.7	-4'.6
v 4.3	+3'.0		
GHA Moon	248°25'.9		N22°10'.9
C long W	-167°25'.9	HP 60.4	
LHA Moon	81°		

Hc	21°44'	SA	20°42'.5
d +40	+7	IE and dip	-1'.4
		AA	20°41'.1
CA	21°51'	Corrn	+62'.0
		HP LL	+8'.2
Z	80°	TA	21°51'.3
Zn	**280°** (360°-Z)	CA	21°51'.0
		Intercept	**0'.3** T

9.8

	h m		
Dusk twilight	20 16 LMT 23d		
Long E as time	-5 21		
	14 55 GMT 23d		
GHA Moon 14h	283°58'.8	DEC	N14 10'.0
Incre 54m 32s	+13°00'.7	d 11.2	+10'.2
v 10.0	+9'.1		
GHA Moon	297°08'.6		N14 20'.2
C long E	+79°51'.4	HP 58.4	
	377°		
-360°	-360°		
LHA Moon	17°		

Hc	28°04'	SA	27°27'.3
d -58	19'	IE and dip	-4'.2
		AA	27°23'.1
CA	27°45'	Corrn	+60'.0
		HP UL	+4'.0
Z	161°		28°27'.1
Zn	**341°** (180°+Z)	-30'	-30'.0
		TA	27°57'.1
		CA	27°45'.0
		Intercept	**12'.1** T

9.9

	h m		
Dusk twilight	20 21 LMT 22d		
Long W as time	+3 57		
	00 18 GMT 23d		
GHA Moon 00h	81°02'.7	DEC	N11°27'.4
Incre 17m 41s	+4°13'.2	d 11.9	+3'.5
v 11.3	+3'.3		N11°30'.9
GHA Moon	85°19'.2		
C long W	-59°19'.2	HP 57.8	
LHA Moon	26°		

Hc	28°24'	SA	26°57'.6
d -56	-29'	IE and dip	+0'.3
		AA	26°57'.9
CA	27°55'	Corrn	+60'.1
		HP UL	+3'.6
Z	151°		28°01'.6
Zn	**331°** (180°+Z)	-30'	-30'.0
		TA	27°31'.6
		CA	27°55'.0
		Intercept	**23'.4** A

9.10

	h m s		
	20 16 06+ ZT 12d		
Zone +11	+11		
	07 16 06 GMT 13d		
GHA Moon 07h	253°25'.4	DEC	N24°07'.3
Incre 16m 06s	+3°50'.5	d 2.7	-0'.7
v 3.0	+0'.8		N24°06'.6
GHA Moon	257°16'.7		
C long W	-160°16'.7	HP 60.5	
LHA Moon	97°		

Hc	12°26'	SA	11°20'.1
d +42	+5	IE and dip	+0'.2
		AA	11°20'.3
CA	12°31	Corrn	+62'.5
		HP LL	+8'.5
Z	68°	TA	12°31'.3
Zn	**292°** (360°-Z)	CA	12°31'.0
		Intercept	**0'.3** A

CHAPTER 10

10.1 (a)

	h m
Dawn twilight	03 32 LMT 14d
Long W as time	+9
Approx time	**03 41 GMT 14d**

(b)

GHA Aries 03h	306°50'.9	DR Lat	45°40'.6N
Incre 41m	+10°16'.7	a_0	-49'.6
GHA Aries	317°07'.6		44°51'.0
DR long W	-2°15'.0	+1°	+1°
LHA Aries	314°52'.6	**Approx Angle**	**45°51'.0**

10.2

	h m
Dusk twilight	17 59 LMT 7d
Long W as time	+1 18
	19 17 GMT 7d

GHA Aries 19h	300°51'.3		
Incre 17m 30s	+4°23'.2		
GHA Aries	305°14'.5		
DR long W	-19°29'.0		
LHA Aries	285°45'.5	Azimuth	001° T
		(from Polaris azimuth table)	
		True bearing	001° T
		Variation W	+12°
		Magnetic bearing	013° M
		Compass bearing	019° C
		Magnetic bearing	-013° M
		Deviation	**6° W**

10.3

	h m
Dusk twilight	17 58 LMT 7d
Long W as time	+30
	18 28 GMT 7d

GHA Aries 18h	285°48'.8	SA	46°17'.3
Incre 28m 40s	+7°11'.2	IE and dip	-3'.6
GHA Aries	293°00'.0	AA	46°13'.7
DR long W	-7°29'.9	Corrn	-0'.9
		TA	46°12'.8
LHA Aries	285°30'.1	a_0	+1°14'.3
		a_1	+0'.5
		a_2	+0'.9
			47°28'.5
		-1°	-1°
		Latitude	**46°28'.5N**

10.4

	h m		
Dawn twilight	04 14 LMT 13d		
Long W as time	+3 27		
	07 41 GMT 13d		
GHA Aries 07h	06°01'.6	SA	35°24'.1
Incre 41h 03s	+10°17'.4	IE and dip	-5'.4
GHA Aries	16°19'.0	AA	35°18'.7
+360°	+360°	Corrn	-1'.4
	376°19'.0	TA	35°17'.3
DR long W	-51°45'.1	a_0	+41'.9
		a_1	+0'.5
LHA Aries	324°33'.9	a_2	+0'.3
			36°00'.0
		-1°	-1°
		Latitude	**35°00'.0N**

10.5

	h m		
Dawn twilight	04 43 LMT 13d		
Long E as time	-10 20		
	18 23 GMT 12d		
GHA Aries 18h	170°29'.6	SA	25°21'.3
Incre 28m 12s	+7°04'.2	IE and dip	-1'.0
GHA Aries	177°33'.8	AA	25°20'.3
DR long E	+155°01'.9	Corrn	-2'.0
		TA	25°18'.3
LHA Aries	332°35'.7	a_0	+35'.6
		a_1	+0'.4
		a_2	+0'.2
			25°54'.5
		-1°	-1°
		Latitude	**24°54'.5N**

10.6

	h m		
Dawn twilight	04 57 LMT 14d		
Long W as time	+3 20		
	08 17 GMT 14d		
GHA Aries 08h	22°03'.2	SA	20°13'.6
Incre 17m 01s	+4°15'.9	IE and dip	-3'.4
GHA Aries	26°19'.1	AA	20°10'.2
+360°	+360°	Corrn	-2'.6
	386°19'.1	TA	20°07'.6
DR long W	50°06'.7	a_0	+33'.0
		a_1	+0'.4
LHA Aries	336°12'.4	a_2	+0'.2
			20°41'.2
		-1°	-1°
		Latitude	**19°41'.2N**

10.7

	h m		
Dusk twilight	17 57 LMT 7d		
Long W as time	+48		
	18 45 GMT 7d		
GHA Aries 18h	285°48'.8	SA	52°30'.7
Incre 54m 05s	+13°33'.5	IE and dip	-4'.8
GHA Aries	299°22'.3	AA	52°25'.9
DR long W	-12°07'.4	Corrn	-0'.7
LHA Aries	287°14'.9	TA	52°25'.2
		a_0	+1°12'.9
		a_1	+0'.6
		a_2	+0'.9
			53°39'.6
		-1°	-1°
		Latitude	**52°39'.6N**

10.8

	h m		
Dusk twilight	17 57 LMT 8d		
Long W as time	+1 01		
	18 58 GMT 8d		
GHA Aries 18h	286°47'.9	SA	50°05'.7
Incre 55m 47s	+13°59'.0	IE and dip	+1'.2
GHA Aries	300°46'.9	AA	50°06'.9
DR long W	-15°10'.1	Corrn	-0'.8
LHA Aries	285°36'.8	TA	50°06'.1
		a_0	+1°14'.2
		a_1	+0'.6
		a_2	+0'.9
			51°21'.8
		-1°	-1°
		Latitude	**50°21'.8N**

10.9

	h m		
Dawn twilight	03 58 LMT 14d		
Long E as time	-10 41		
	17 17 GMT 13d		
GHA Aries 17h	156°26'.2	SA	40°10'.4
Incre 17m 50s	+4°28'.2	IE and dip	+1'.0
GHA Aries	160°54'.4	AA	40°11'.4
DR long E	+160°12'.4	Corrn	-1'.1
LHA Aries	321°06'.8	TA	40°10'.3
		a_0	+44'.6
		a_1	+0'.5
		a_2	+0'.3
			40°55'.7
		-1°	-1°
		Latitude	**39°55'.7N**

10.10

	h m
Dusk twilight	17 59 LMT 7d
Long W as time	+28
	18 27 GMT 7d

GHA Aries 18h	285°48'.8	SA	42°10'.9
Incre 29m 40s	+7°26'.2	IE and dip	-5'.1
GHA Aries	293°15'.0	AA	42°05'.8
DR long W	-6°59'.4	Corrn	-1'.1
		TA	42°04'.7
LHA Aries	286°15'.6	a_0	+1°13'.7
		a_1	+0'.5
		a_2	+0'.9
			43°19'.8
		-1°	-1°
		Latitude	**42°19'.8N**

CHAPTER 11

11.1

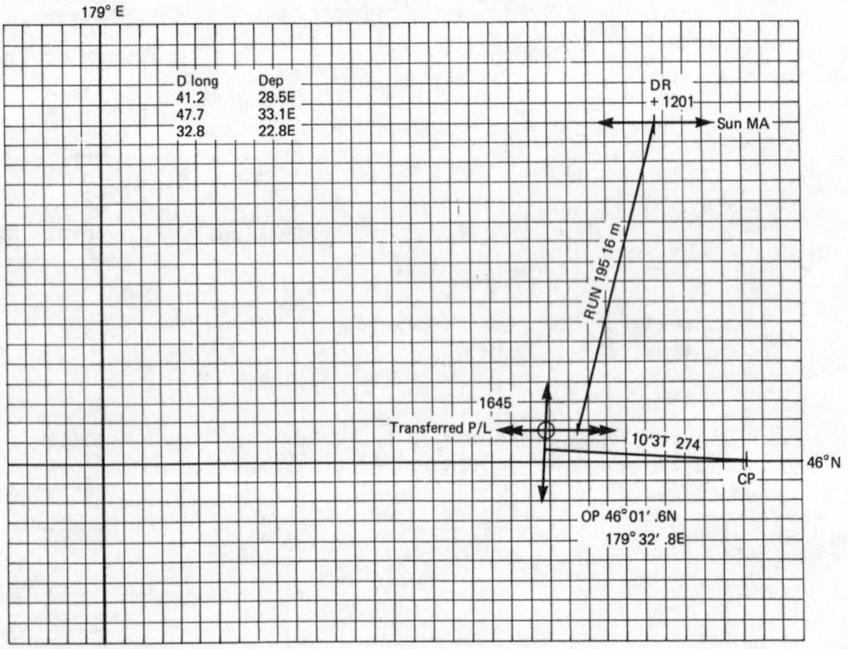

11.2

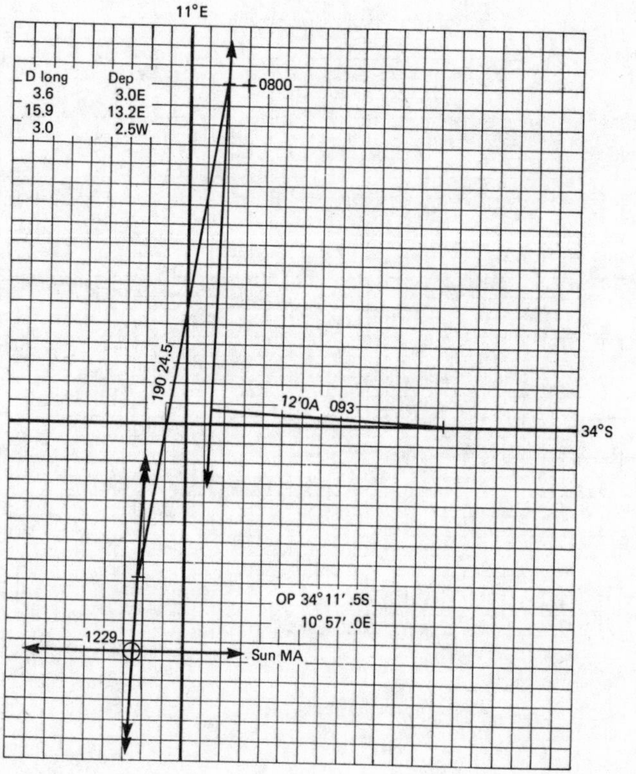
11°E
D long
3.6
15.9
3.0
Dep
3.0E
13.2E
2.5W
0800
190 24.5
12'0A 093
34°S
OP 34° 11'.5S
10° 57'.0E
1229
Sun MA

11.3

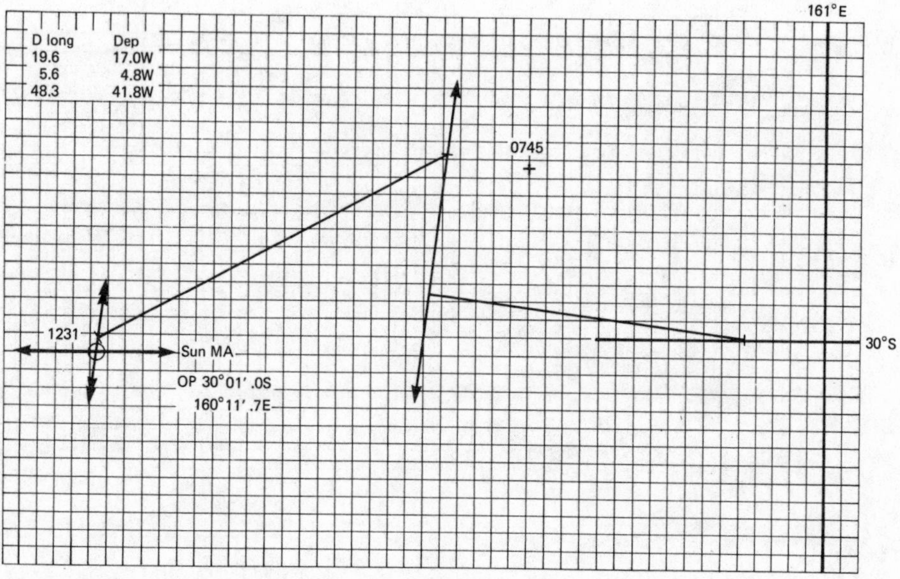
161°E
D long
19.6
5.6
48.3
Dep
17.0W
4.8W
41.8W
0745
1231
Sun MA
OP 30° 01'.0S
160° 11'.7E
30°S

11.4

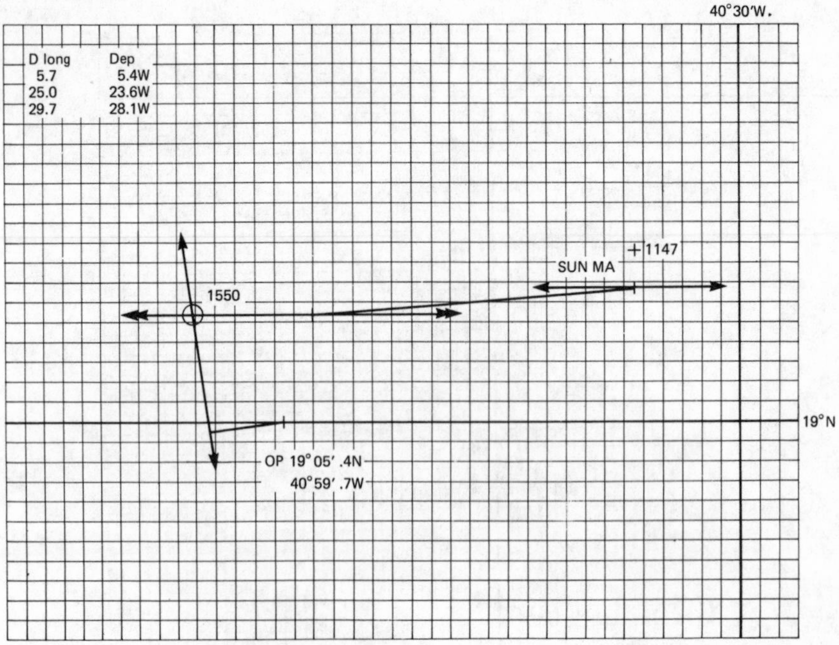
40°30'W.
D long
5.7
25.0
29.7
Dep
5.4W
23.6W
28.1W
1147
SUN MA
1550
19°N
OP 19°05'.4N
40°59'.7W

11.5

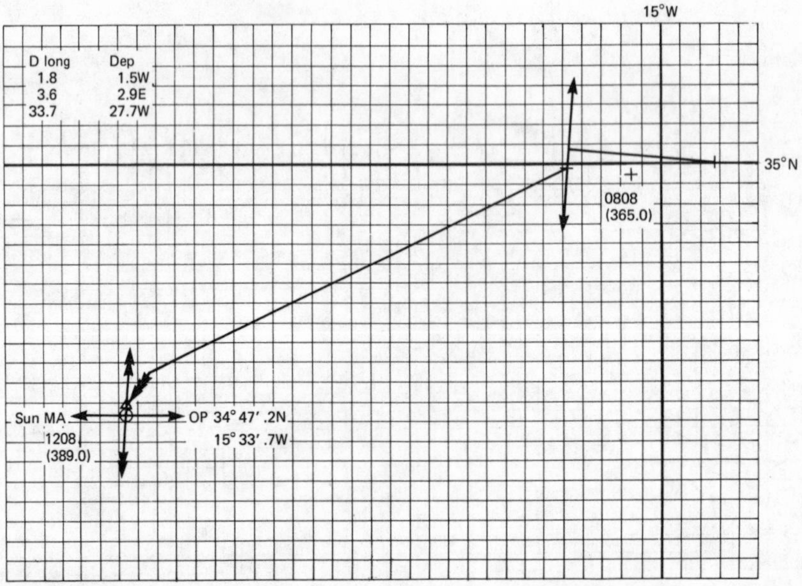
15°W
D long
1.8
3.6
33.7
Dep
1.5W
2.9E
27.7W
35°N
0808
(365.0)
Sun MA
1208
(389.0)
OP 34°47'.2N
15°33'.7W

11.6

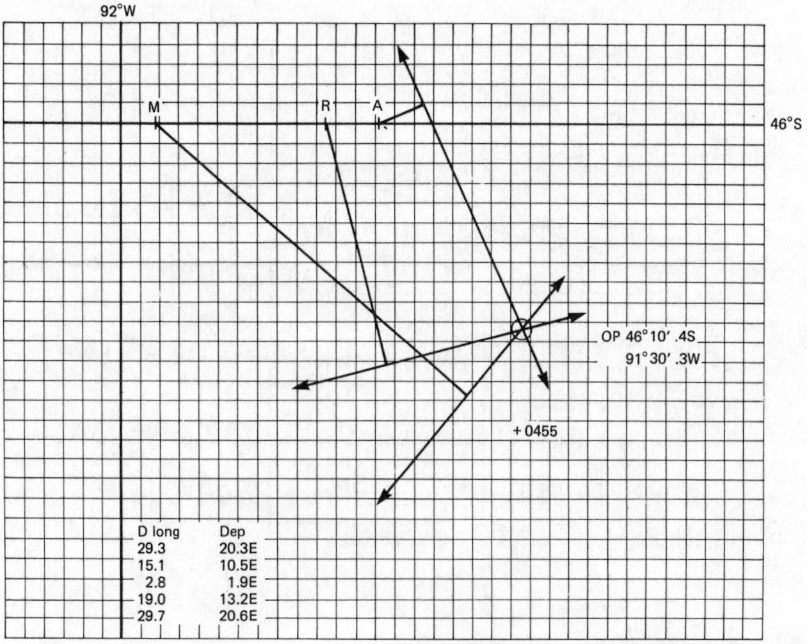
92°W
46°S
M
R
A
OP 46°10′.4S
91°30′.3W
+0455
D long
29.3
15.1
2.8
19.0
29.7
Dep
20.3E
10.5E
1.9E
13.2E
20.6E

11.7

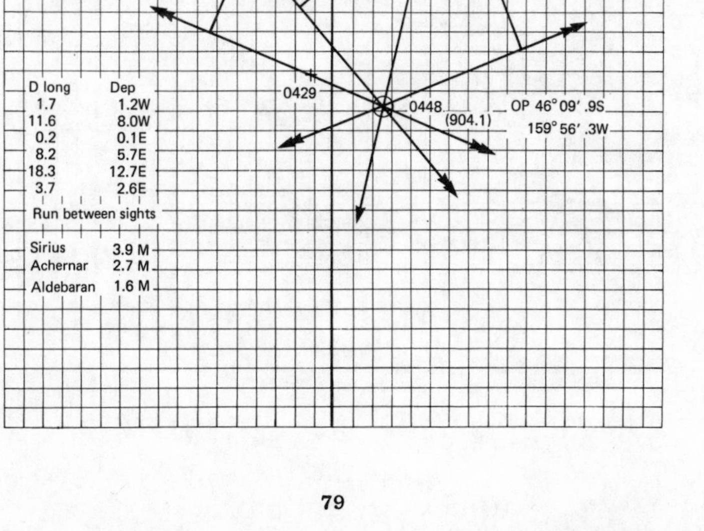
160°W
46°S
SI
AC
AL
SU
3.9
2.7
1.6
0429
0448
(904.1)
OP 46°09′.9S
159°56′.3W
D long
1.7
11.6
0.2
8.2
18.3
3.7
Dep
1.2W
8.0W
0.1E
5.7E
12.7E
2.6E
Run between sights
Sirius 3.9 M
Achernar 2.7 M
Aldebaran 1.6 M

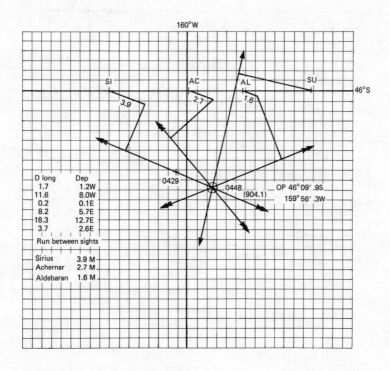

11.8

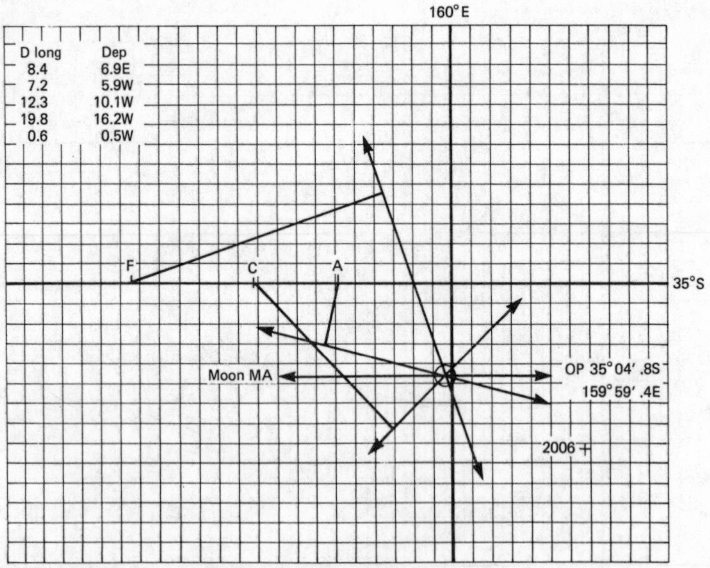
160°E
D long
8.4
7.2
12.3
19.8
0.6
Dep
6.9E
5.9W
10.1W
16.2W
0.5W
F
C
A
35°S
Moon MA
OP 35°04'.8S
159°59'.4E
2006

11.9

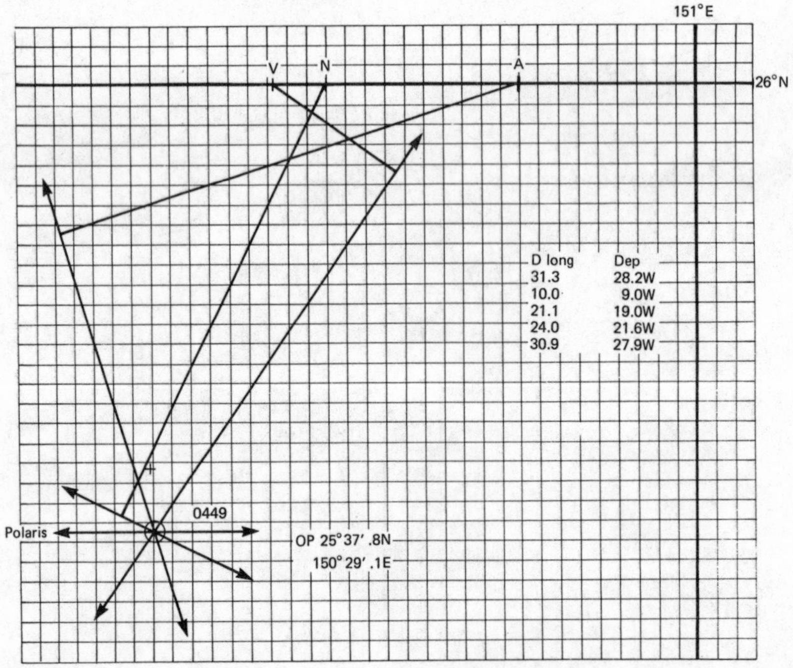
151°E
V
N
A
26°N
D long
31.3
10.0
21.1
24.0
30.9
Dep
28.2W
9.0W
19.0W
21.6W
27.9W
0449
Polaris
OP 25°37'.8N
150°29'.1E

11.10

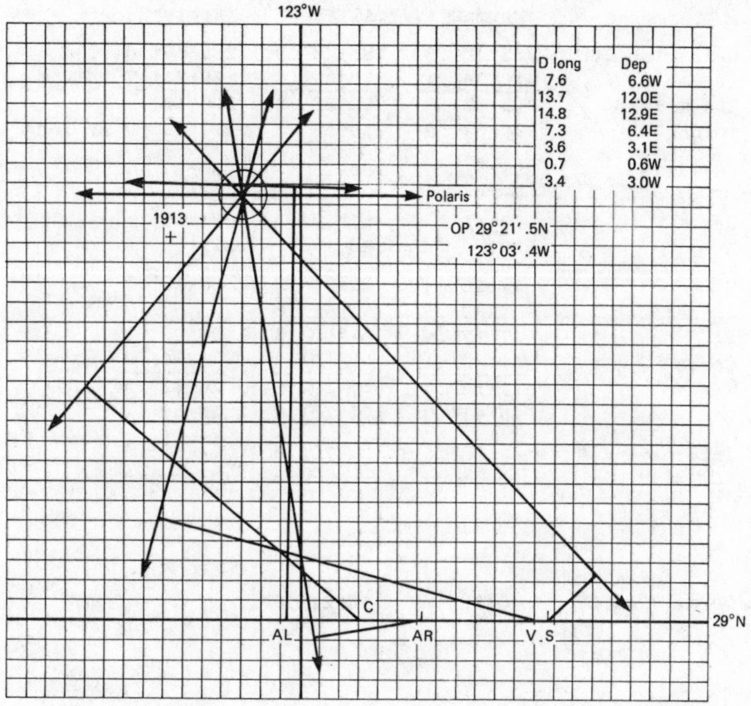

CHAPTER 12

12.1 (a)

	h m	
Dusk twilight	17 58	LMT 7d
Long W as time	+42	
	18 40	GMT 7d

GHA Aries 18h	285°48'.8
Incre 40m	+10°01'.6
GHA Aries	295°50'.4
DR long W	-10°31'.2
LHA Aries	285°19'.2 (use 285°)

Stars available:

	Hc	Zn
◇ **Mirfak**	**16°41'**	**033°**
Alpheratz	**29°07'**	**077°**
◇ **ALTAIR**	**51°19'**	**160°**
Rasalhague	**51°58'**	**215°**
◇ **ARCTURUS**	**26°37'**	**271°**
Alkaid	**39°39'**	**304°**
Kochab	**51°16'**	**337°**
Polaris	**46°14'.6**	**001°** (from Polaris tables)

DR lat	46°29'.1N
$-a_0$	-1°14'.5
	45°14'.6
+1°	+1°
	46°14'.6

(b)

	Mirfak	Altair	Arcturus		Polaris
GHA Aries 18h	285°48'.8	285°48'.8	285°48'.8		285°48'.8
Incre	+10°04'.1	+10°09'.4	+10°21'.7		+10°29'.2
GHA Aries	295°52'.9	295°58'.2	296°10'.5		296°18'.0
C long W	-10°52'.9	-10°58'.2	-10°10'.5	EP long	-10°29'.8
LHA Aries	285°	285°	286°		285°48'.2
Hc	16°41'	51°19'	25°55'		
Zn	033°	160°	271°		
SA	17°18'.4	51°01'.2	26°10'.3		46°14'.6
IE and dip	-0'.8	-0'.8	-0'.8		-0'.8
AA	17°17'.6	51°00'.4	26°09'.5		46°13'.8
Corrn	-3'.1	-0'.8	-2'.0		-0'.9
TA	17°14'.5	50°59'.6	26°07'.5		46°12'.9
CA	16°41'.0	51°19'.0	25°55'.0	a_0	+1°14'.1
Intercept	33'.5 T	19'.4 A	12'.5 T	a_1	+0'.5
				a_2	+0'.9
					47°28'.4
					-1°
				Latitude	46°28'.4N

OP at 1740 ZT 46°28'.4N 10°27'.6W.

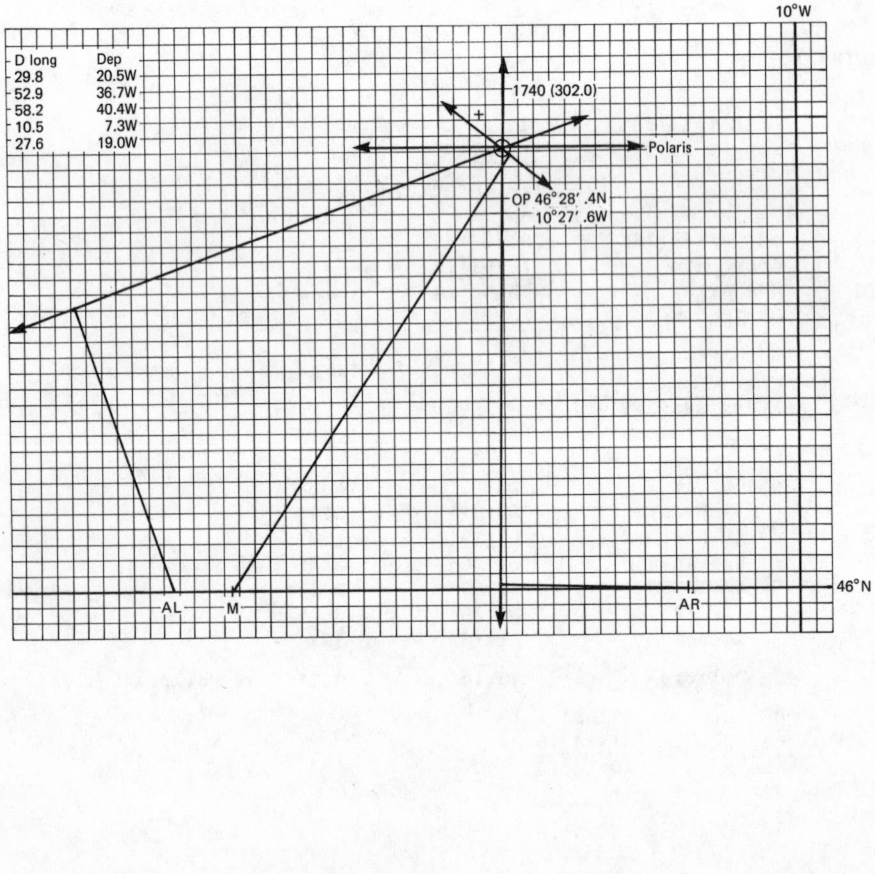

(c) EP at 0516 ZT 45°37'.7N 10°44'.9W (by traverse tables).

Course	Dist	D lat N	D lat S	Dep E	Dep W
195°	46.5M	-	44.9	-	12.0
180°	5.8M	-	5.8	-	-
			50.7		12.0

OP (1740 ZT) lat	46°28'.4N	OP long	10°27'.6W
D lat	-50'.7S	D long	+17'.3W*
EP (0516 ZT) lat	45°37'.7N	EP long	10°44'.9W

*D long for dep of 12'.0 at a mid latitude of 46°03'.0.

	h m
Dawn twilight	05 36 LMT 8d
Long W as time	+43
	06 19 GMT 8d

	Dubhe	Sirius	Mirfak
GHA Aries 06h	106°18'.4	106°18'.4	106°18'.4
Incre	+4°06'.9	+4°13'.2	+4°19'.5
GHA Aries	110°25'.3	110°31'.6	110°37'.9
C long W	-10°25'.3	-10°31'.6	-10°37'.9
LHA Aries	100°	100°	100°
Hc	50°16'	27°18'	57°24'
Zn	042°	179°	295°

GHA Venus 06h	313°46'.4	DEC	N8°13'.0
Incre	+4°28'.8	d 0.2	-0'.1
v 0.7	+0'.2		N8°12'.9
GHA Venus	318°15'.4		
C long W	-10°15'.4		
LHA Venus	308°		

Hc		31°35'
d	+45	+10
CA		31°45'

Z	114°
Zn	114°

	Dubhe	Sirius	Mirfak
SA	49°52'.2	27°40'.6	57°22'.0
IE and dip	-0'.8	-0'.8	-0'.8
AA	49°51'.4	27°39'.8	57°21'.2
Corrn	-0'.8	-1'.8	-0'.6
TA	49°50'.6	27°38'.0	57°20'.6
CA	50°16'.0	27°18'.0	57°24'.0
Intercept	25'.4 A	20'.0 T	3'.4 A

	Venus
SA	31°35'.1
IE and dip	-0'.8
AA	31°34'.3
Corrn	-1'.6
	31°32'.7
Add corrn	+0'.3
TA	31°33'.0
CA	31°45'.0
Intercept	12'.0 A

OP at 0516 ZT 45°39'.9N 10°47'.4W.

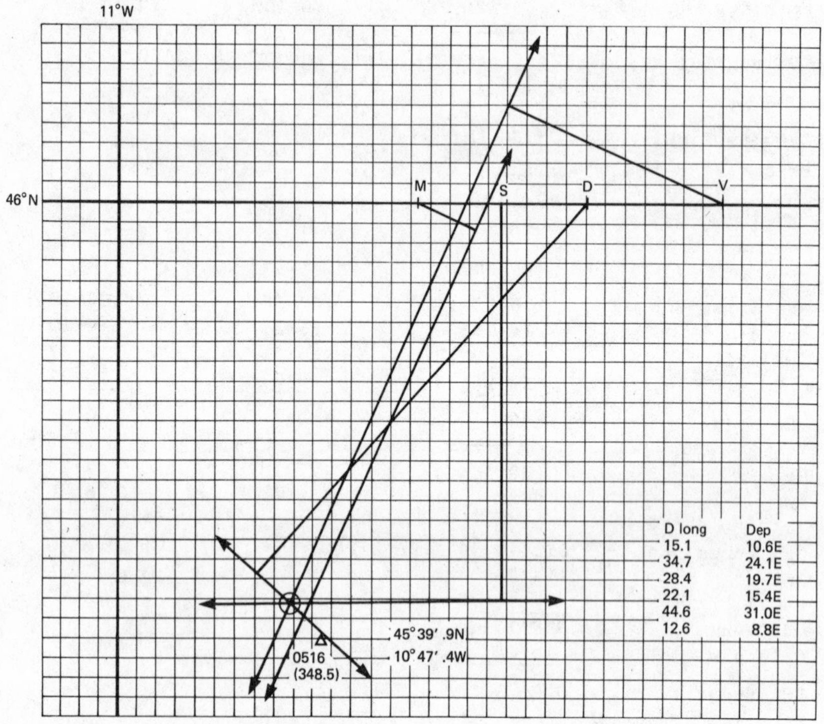

(d)

Course	Dist	D lat N	D lat S	Dep E	Dep W
195°	8	-	7.7	-	2.1
180°	1	-	1.0	-	-
			8.7		2.1

OP (0516 ZT) lat	45°39'.9N	OP long	10°47'.4W
D lat	-8'.7S	D long	+3'.0W*
EP (0717 ZT) lat	45°31'.2N	EP long	10°50'.4W

*D long for a Dep of 2.1 at mid latitude of 45°35'.6N.

Answers

GHA Sun 08h	303°04'.1	DEC	S5°42'.3
Incre 17h 40m	+4°25'.0	d 1.0	+0'.3
GHA Sun	307°29'.1		S5°42'.6
C long W	-10°29'.1		
LHA Sun	297°		

Hc		14°34'	SA	13°48'.1
d	-46	-33'	IE and dip	-0'.8
		14°01'	AA	13°47'.3
			Corrn LL	+12'.4
			TA	13°59'.7
			CA	14°01'.0
			Intercept	1'.3 A

Run 195° T 17.0M, current 180° T 2.1M.

EP at 1131 ZT 45°12'.3N 10°55'.7W.

DEC	S5°46'.1	SA	39°19'.6
d 1.0	+0'.5*	IE and dip	-0'.8
	S5°46'.6	AA	39°18'.8
		Corrn UL	-17'.2
		TA	39°01'.6
		From 90°	90°
		TZD	50°58'.4
		DEC	-5°46'.6
		Latitude	45°11'.8N

*By interpolation as no increment tables are available.

OP at 1131 ZT 45°11'.8N 10°56'.0W.

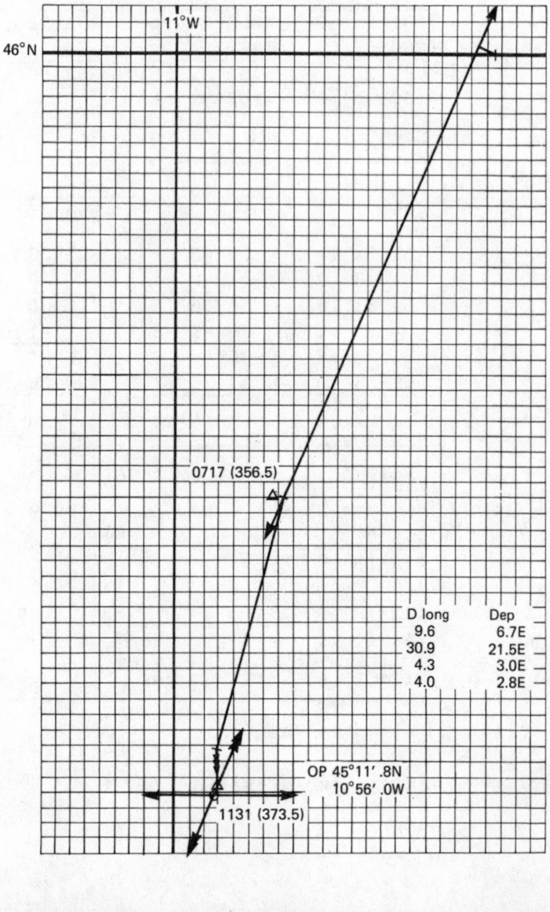

(e) Departure point 46° N 10°40'W (lat A)

Destination 28°08'N 15°40'W (lat B)

Difference of longitude 5°

Using AP 3270 extracts:

Difference of long = LHA = 5°

Lat A = latitude = 46° N

Lat B = declination = 28°08'N

Hc	71°34'	Z	166°
d +59	+8	Zn	194° (360°-Z)
CA	71°42'		
From 90°	90°		
CZD	18°18' = 1098' = 1098M		

Great circle distance 1098M.

Initial course 194°.

12.2 (a)

	h m
	03 20 ZT 12d
Zone +10	+10
	13 20 GMT 12d

	Enif	Rasalhague	Alphecca	Altair
GHA Aries 13h	95°17'.2	95°17'.2	95°17'.2	95°17'.2
Incre	+7°08'.7	+7°13'.9	+7°22'.5	+7°30'.5
GHA Aries	102°25'.9	102°31'.1	102°39'.7	102°47'.7
+360°	+360°	+360°	+360°	+360°
	462°25'.9	462°31'.1	462°39'.7	462°47'.7
C long W	-150°25'.9	-150°31'.1	-150°39'.7	-149°47'.7
LHA Aries	312°	312°	312°	313°
Hc	51°55'	37°20'	26°36'	50°31'
Zn	157°	247°	282°	205°
SA	51°31'.2	36°55'.9	26°23'.2	50°09'.5
IE and dip	+0'.4	+0'.4	+0'.4	+0'.4
AA	51°31'.6	36°56'.3	26°23'.6	50°09'.9
Corrn	-0'.8	-1'.3	-1'.9	-0'.8
TA	51°30'.8	36°55'.0	26°21'.7	50°09'.1
CA	51°55'.0	37°20'.0	26°36'.0	50°31'.0
Intercept	24'.2 A	25'.0 A	14'.3 A	21'.9 A

	Polaris
GHA Aries 13h	95°17'.2
Incre	+7°01'.4
GHA Aries	102°18'.6
+360°	+360°
	462°18'.6
DR long W	-150°14'.8
LHA Aries	312°03'.8

SA	46°38'.7
IE and dip	+0'.4
AA	46°39'.1
Corrn	-0'.9
TA	46°38'.2
a_0	+52'.2
a_1	+0'.5
a_2	+0'.3
	47°31'.2
-1°	-1°
Latitude	46°31'.2N

OP at 0328 ZT 46°31'.2N 150°10'.7W.

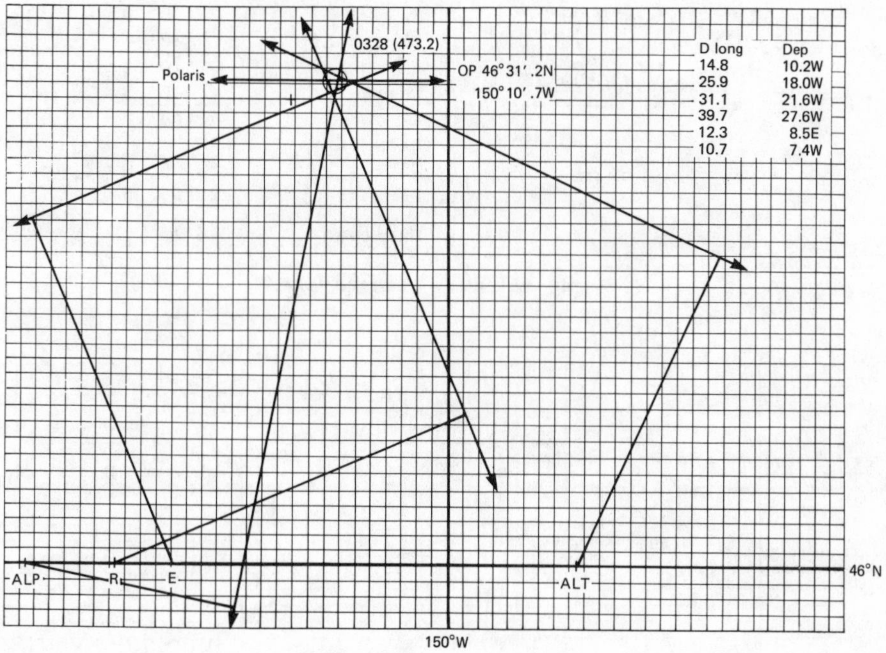

(b) Run 110° T 19M, current 090° T 1.75M.

EP at 0655 ZT 46°24'.8N 149°42'.5W.

GHA Sun 16h	60°04'.3	DEC	N23°08'.6
Incre 55m 49s	+13°57'.3	d 0.1	+0'.1
GHA Sun	74°01'.6		N23°08'.7
+360°	+360°		
	434°01'.6		
C long W	150°01'.6		
LHA Sun	284°		

Hc		25°50'	SA	26°02'.0
d	+40	+6	IE and dip	+0'.4
CA		25°56'	AA	26°02'.4
			Corrn LL	+14'.1
Z		83°	TA	26°16'.5
Zn		083°	CA	25°56'.0
			Intercept	20'.5 T

Run to meridian passage 110° T 32.0M, current 090° T 2.5M.

EP at 1155 ZT 46°14'.0N 148°49'.3W.

	h m	
Meridian passage	12 00	LMT 12d
Long W as time	+9 55	
	21 55	GMT 12d

DEC	N23°09'.4	SA	67°09'.9
d 0.1	+0'.1	IE and dip	+0'.4
	N23°09'.5	AA	67°10'.3
		Corrn UL	-16'.3
		TA	66°54'.0
		From 90°	90°
		TZD	23°06'.0
		DEC	23°09'.5
		Latitude	46°15'.5N

OP at 1155 ZT 46°15'.5N 148°49'.6W.

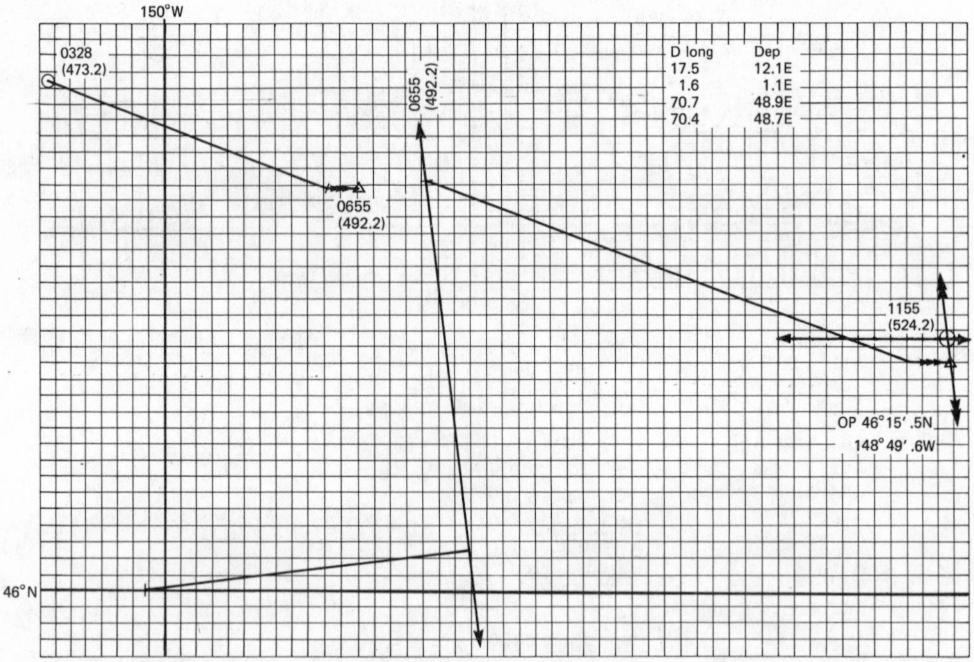

(c) Run 110° T 18.0M, current 090° T 1.5M.

EP at 1500 ZT 46°09'.3N 148°23'.0W.

GHA Sun 01h	195°03'.2	DEC	N23°10'.0
C long W	-148°03'.2		
LHA Sun	47°		

Hc		45°49'	SA	45°51'.9
d	+41	+7	IE and dip	+0'.4
CA		45°56'	AA	45°52'.3
			Corrn LL	+15'.1
Z		105°	TA	46°07'.4
Zn		255° (360°-Z)	CA	45°56'.0
			Intercept	11'.4 T

OP at 1500 46°09'.3N 148°23'.5W.

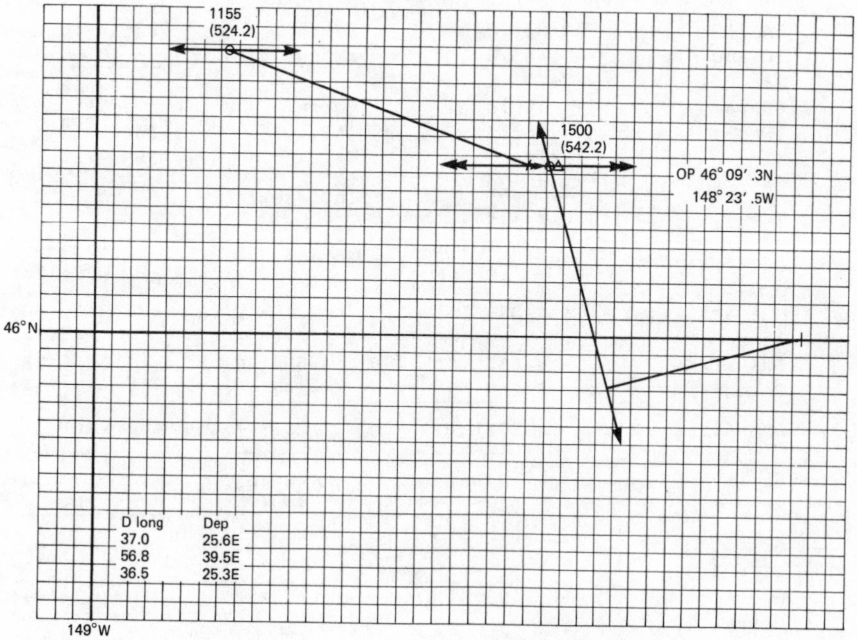

(d) Run 110° T 30.8M, current 090° T 2.6M.

EP at 2016 ZT 45°58'.9N 147°38'.6W.

	h m
Dusk twilight	20 30 LMT 12d
Long W as time	+9 51
	06 21 GMT 13d

Moon

GHA Moon 06h	239°03'.5
Incre 16m 05s	+3°50'.3
v 2.9	+0'.8
GHA Moon	242°54'.6
C long W	-147°54'.6
LHA Moon	95°
DEC	N24°09'.8
d 2.5	-0'.7
	N24°09'.1

Hc		13°44'
d	+42	+6
CA		13°50'
Z		70°
Zn		290°(360°-Z)

Saturn

GHA Saturn 06h	144°02'.4
Incre 16m 40s	+4°10'.0
v 2.5	+0'.7
GHA Saturn	148°13'.1
C long W	-147°13'.1
LHA Saturn	1°
DEC	S8°18'.6
d 0.0	

Hc		36°00'
d	-60	-19'
CA		35°41'
Z		179°
Zn		181°(360°-Z)

	Moon		Saturn
SA	12°23'.2	SA	35°44'.6
IE and dip	+0'.4	IE and dip	+0'.4
AA	2°23'.6	AA	35°45'.0
Corrn	+62'.6	Corrn	-1'.3
HP	+8'.5	AA	35°43'.7
TA	13°34'.7	CA	35°41'.0
CA	13°50'.0	Intercept	2'.7 T
Intercept	15'.3 A		

	Deneb	Arcturus	Pollux
GHA Aries 06h	350°59'.1	350°59'.1	350°59'.1
Incre	+4°14'.4	+4°18'.2	+4°24'.5
GHA Aries	355°13'.5	355°17'.3	355°23'.6
C long W	-147°13'.5	-147°17'.3	-147°23'.6
LHA Aries	208°	208°	208°
Hc	24°01'	62°51'	18°33'
Zn	049°	168°	292°
SA	23°50'.6	62°51'.9	18°40'.6
IE and dip	+0'.4	+0'.4	+0'.4
AA	23°51'.0	62°52'.3	18°41'.0
Corrn	-2'.2	-0'.5	-2'.8
TA	23°48'.8	62°51'.8	18°38'.2
CA	24°01'.0	62°51'.0	18°33'.0
Intercept	12'.2 A	0'.8 T	5'.2 T

OP at 2016 ZT 45°57'.0N 147°33'.2W.

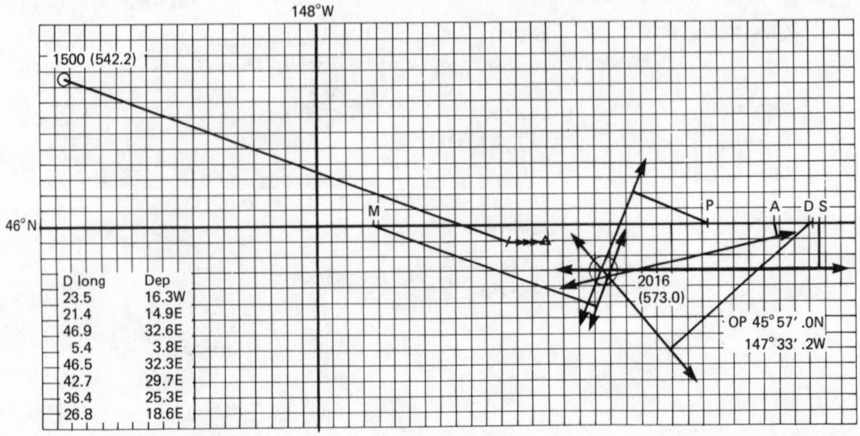

(e) OP at 0328 ZT 46°31'.2N 150°10'.7W log 473.2.

OP at 2016 ZT 45°57'.0N 147°33'.2W log 573.0.

Course		Dist	D lat		Dep	
			N	S	E	W
Total			-	34.2	109.5	-
Run	110°	99.8	-	34.2	94.0	-
Current	090°	15.5	-	-	15.5	-

A drift of 15.5 M for 16h 48m gives a mean current of 090° T 0.9 k.

(f) Departure point 46° N 147°33'W

Destination 10°25'N 109°33'W

Difference of longitude = 38°

Using AP 3270 extracts:

LHA = 360° - difference of longitude = 322°
(LHA is measured westwards.)

Lat = 46° N

DEC = 10°25'N

Hc	41°36'		Z	126°
d +49	20'		Zn	126°
CA	41°56'			
From 90°	-90°			
CZD	48°04' = 2884' = 2884 M			

Great circle distance 2884 M.

Initial course 126°.

Extracts for Exercises

A2 ALTITUDE CORRECTION TABLES 10°-90°—SUN, STARS, PLANETS

SUN

OCT.—MAR. App. Alt.	Lower Limb	Upper Limb	APR.—SEPT. App. Alt.	Lower Limb	Upper Limb
° ′	′	′	° ′	′	′
9 34	+10·8	−21·5	9 39	+10·6	−21·2
9 45	+10·9	−21·4	9 51	+10·7	−21·1
9 56	+11·0	−21·3	10 03	+10·8	−21·0
10 08	+11·1	−21·2	10 15	+10·9	−20·9
10 21	+11·2	−21·1	10 27	+11·0	−20·8
10 34	+11·3	−21·0	10 40	+11·1	−20·7
10 47	+11·4	−20·9	10 54	+11·2	−20·6
11 01	+11·5	−20·8	11 08	+11·3	−20·5
11 15	+11·6	−20·7	11 23	+11·4	−20·4
11 30	+11·7	−20·6	11 38	+11·5	−20·3
11 46	+11·8	−20·5	11 54	+11·6	−20·2
12 02	+11·9	−20·4	12 10	+11·7	−20·1
12 19	+12·0	−20·3	12 28	+11·8	−20·0
12 37	+12·1	−20·2	12 46	+11·9	−19·9
12 55	+12·2	−20·1	13 05	+12·0	−19·8
13 14	+12·3	−20·0	13 24	+12·1	−19·7
13 35	+12·4	−19·9	13 45	+12·2	−19·6
13 56	+12·5	−19·8	14 07	+12·3	−19·5
14 18	+12·6	−19·7	14 30	+12·4	−19·4
14 42	+12·7	−19·6	14 54	+12·5	−19·3
15 06	+12·8	−19·5	15 19	+12·6	−19·2
15 32	+12·9	−19·4	15 46	+12·7	−19·1
15 59	+13·0	−19·3	16 14	+12·8	−19·0
16 28	+13·1	−19·2	16 44	+12·9	−18·9
16 59	+13·2	−19·1	17 15	+13·0	−18·8
17 32	+13·3	−19·0	17 48	+13·1	−18·7
18 06	+13·4	−18·9	18 24	+13·2	−18·6
18 42	+13·5	−18·8	19 01	+13·3	−18·5
19 21	+13·6	−18·7	19 42	+13·4	−18·4
20 03	+13·7	−18·6	20 25	+13·5	−18·3
20 48	+13·8	−18·5	21 11	+13·6	−18·2
21 35	+13·9	−18·4	22 00	+13·7	−18·1
22 26	+14·0	−18·3	22 54	+13·8	−18·0
23 22	+14·1	−18·2	23 51	+13·9	−17·9
24 21	+14·2	−18·1	24 53	+14·0	−17·8
25 26	+14·3	−18·0	26 00	+14·1	−17·7
26 36	+14·4	−17·9	27 13	+14·2	−17·6
27 52	+14·5	−17·8	28 33	+14·3	−17·5
29 15	+14·6	−17·7	30 00	+14·4	−17·4
30 46	+14·7	−17·6	31 35	+14·5	−17·3
32 26	+14·8	−17·5	33 20	+14·6	−17·2
34 17	+14·9	−17·4	35 17	+14·7	−17·1
36 20	+15·0	−17·3	37 26	+14·8	−17·0
38 36	+15·1	−17·2	39 50	+14·9	−16·9
41 08	+15·2	−17·1	42 31	+15·0	−16·8
43 59	+15·3	−17·0	45 31	+15·1	−16·7
47 10	+15·4	−16·9	48 55	+15·2	−16·6
50 46	+15·5	−16·8	52 44	+15·3	−16·5
54 49	+15·6	−16·7	57 02	+15·4	−16·4
59 23	+15·7	−16·6	61 51	+15·5	−16·3
64 30	+15·8	−16·5	67 17	+15·6	−16·2
70 12	+15·9	−16·4	73 16	+15·7	−16·1
76 26	+16·0	−16·3	79 43	+15·8	−16·0
83 05	+16·1	−16·2	86 32	+15·9	−15·9
90 00			90 00		

STARS AND PLANETS

App. Alt.	Corrⁿ
° ′	′
9 56	−5·3
10 08	−5·2
10 20	−5·1
10 33	−5·0
10 46	−4·9
11 00	−4·8
11 14	−4·7
11 29	−4·6
11 45	−4·5
12 01	−4·4
12 18	−4·3
12 35	−4·2
12 54	−4·1
13 13	−4·0
13 33	−3·9
13 54	−3·8
14 16	−3·7
14 40	−3·6
15 04	−3·5
15 30	−3·4
15 57	−3·3
16 26	−3·2
16 56	−3·1
17 28	−3·0
18 02	−2·9
18 38	−2·8
19 17	−2·7
19 58	−2·6
20 42	−2·5
21 28	−2·4
22 19	−2·3
23 13	−2·2
24 11	−2·1
25 14	−2·0
26 22	−1·9
27 36	−1·8
28 56	−1·7
30 24	−1·6
32 00	−1·5
33 45	−1·4
35 40	−1·3
37 48	−1·2
40 08	−1·1
42 44	−1·0
45 36	−0·9
48 47	−0·8
52 18	−0·7
56 11	−0·6
60 28	−0·5
65 08	−0·4
70 11	−0·3
75 34	−0·2
81 13	−0·1
87 03	0·0
90 00	

App. Alt. / Additional Corrⁿ

1983

VENUS

	App. Alt. (°)	Additional Corrⁿ (′)
Jan. 1-May 10	0	+0·1
	42	
May 11-June 23	0	+0·2
	47	
June 24-July 19	0	+0·3
	46	
July 20-Aug. 3	0	+0·4
	11	+0·5
	41	
Aug. 4-Aug. 12	0	+0·5
	6	+0·6
	20	+0·7
	31	
Aug. 13-Sept. 7	0	+0·6
	4	+0·7
	12	+0·8
	22	
Sept. 8-Sept. 16	0	+0·5
	6	+0·6
	20	+0·7
	31	
Sept. 17-Oct. 2	0	+0·4
	11	+0·5
	41	
Oct. 3-Oct. 30	0	+0·3
	46	
Oct. 31-Dec. 17	0	+0·2
	47	
Dec. 18-Dec. 31	0	+0·1
	42	

MARS

	App. Alt. (°)	Additional Corrⁿ (′)
Jan. 1-Dec. 31	0	+0·1
	60	

DIP

Ht. of Eye (m)	Corrⁿ (′)	Ht. of Eye (ft.)
2·4	−2·8	8·0
2·6	−2·9	8·6
2·8	−3·0	9·2
3·0	−3·1	9·8
3·2	−3·2	10·5
3·4	−3·3	11·2
3·6	−3·4	11·9
3·8	−3·5	12·6
4·0	−3·6	13·3
4·3	−3·7	14·1
4·5	−3·8	14·9
4·7	−3·9	15·7
5·0	−4·0	16·5
5·2	−4·1	17·4
5·5	−4·2	18·3
5·8	−4·3	19·1
6·1	−4·4	20·1
6·3	−4·5	21·0
6·6	−4·6	22·0
6·9	−4·7	22·9
7·2	−4·8	23·9
7·5	−4·9	24·9
7·9	−5·0	26·0
8·2	−5·1	27·1
8·5	−5·2	28·1
8·8	−5·3	29·2
9·2	−5·4	30·4
9·5	−5·5	31·5
9·9	−5·6	32·7
10·3	−5·7	33·9
10·6	−5·8	35·1
11·0	−5·9	36·3
11·4	−6·0	37·6
11·8	−6·1	38·9
12·2	−6·2	40·1
12·6	−6·3	41·5
13·0	−6·4	42·8
13·4	−6·5	44·2
13·8	−6·6	45·5
14·2	−6·7	46·9
14·7	−6·8	48·4
15·1	−6·9	49·8
15·5	−7·0	51·3
16·0	−7·1	52·8
16·5	−7·2	54·3
16·9	−7·3	55·8
17·4	−7·4	57·4
17·9	−7·5	58·9
18·4	−7·6	60·5
18·8	−7·7	62·1
19·3	−7·8	63·8
19·8	−7·9	65·4
20·4	−8·0	67·1
20·9	−8·1	68·8
21·4		70·5

Ht. of Eye	Corrⁿ
m	′
1·0	−1·8
1·5	−2·2
2·0	−2·5
2·5	−2·8
3·0	−3·0
See table ←	
m	′
20	−7·9
22	−8·3
24	−8·6
26	−9·0
28	−9·3
30	−9·6
32	−10·0
34	−10·3
36	−10·6
38	−10·8
40	−11·1
42	−11·4
44	−11·7
46	−11·9
48	−12·2
ft.	′
2	−1·4
4	−1·9
6	−2·4
8	−2·7
10	−3·1
See table ←	
ft.	′
70	−8·1
75	−8·4
80	−8·7
85	−8·9
90	−9·2
95	−9·5
100	−9·7
105	−9·9
110	−10·2
115	−10·4
120	−10·6
125	−10·8
130	−11·1
135	−11·3
140	−11·5
145	−11·7
150	−11·9
155	−12·1

App. Alt. = Apparent altitude = Sextant altitude corrected for index error and dip.
For daylight observations of Venus, see pages 259 and 260.

ALTITUDE CORRECTION TABLES 0°–35°—MOON

App. Alt.	0°–4° Corrn	5°–9° Corrn	10°–14° Corrn	15°–19° Corrn	20°–24° Corrn	25°–29° Corrn	30°–34° Corrn	App. Alt.
′	° ′	° ′	° ′	° ′	° ′	° ′	° ′	′
00	0 33·8	5 58·2	10 62·1	15 62·8	20 62·2	25 60·8	30 58·9	00
10	35·9	58·5	62·2	62·8	62·1	60·8	58·8	10
20	37·8	58·7	62·2	62·8	62·1	60·7	58·8	20
30	39·6	58·9	62·3	62·8	62·1	60·7	58·7	30
40	41·2	59·1	62·3	62·8	62·0	60·6	58·6	40
50	42·6	59·3	62·4	62·7	62·0	60·6	58·5	50
00	1 44·0	6 59·5	11 62·4	16 62·7	21 62·0	26 60·5	31 58·5	00
10	45·2	59·7	62·4	62·7	61·9	60·4	58·4	10
20	46·3	59·9	62·5	62·7	61·9	60·4	58·3	20
30	47·3	60·0	62·5	62·7	61·9	60·3	58·2	30
40	48·3	60·2	62·5	62·7	61·8	60·3	58·2	40
50	49·2	60·3	62·6	62·7	61·8	60·2	58·1	50
00	2 50·0	7 60·5	12 62·6	17 62·7	22 61·7	27 60·1	32 58·0	00
10	50·8	60·6	62·6	62·6	61·7	60·1	57·9	10
20	51·4	60·7	62·6	62·6	61·6	60·0	57·8	20
30	52·1	60·9	62·7	62·6	61·6	59·9	57·8	30
40	52·7	61·0	62·7	62·6	61·5	59·9	57·7	40
50	53·3	61·1	62·7	62·6	61·5	59·8	57·6	50
00	3 53·8	8 61·2	13 62·7	18 62·5	23 61·5	28 59·7	33 57·5	00
10	54·3	61·3	62·7	62·5	61·4	59·7	57·4	10
20	54·8	61·4	62·7	62·5	61·4	59·6	57·4	20
30	55·2	61·5	62·8	62·5	61·3	59·6	57·3	30
40	55·6	61·6	62·8	62·4	61·3	59·5	57·2	40
50	56·0	61·6	62·8	62·4	61·2	59·4	57·1	50
00	4 56·4	9 61·7	14 62·8	19 62·4	24 61·2	29 59·3	34 57·0	00
10	56·7	61·8	62·8	62·3	61·1	59·3	56·9	10
20	57·1	61·9	62·8	62·3	61·1	59·2	56·9	20
30	57·4	61·9	62·8	62·3	61·0	59·1	56·8	30
40	57·7	62·0	62·8	62·2	60·9	59·1	56·7	40
50	57·9	62·1	62·8	62·2	60·9	59·0	56·6	50

H.P.	L	U	L	U	L	U	L	U	L	U	L	U	L	U	H.P.
′	′	′	′	′	′	′	′	′	′	′	′	′	′	′	′
54·0	0·3	0·9	0·3	0·9	0·4	1·0	0·5	1·1	0·6	1·2	0·7	1·3	0·9	1·5	54·0
54·3	0·7	1·1	0·7	1·2	0·7	1·2	0·8	1·3	0·9	1·4	1·1	1·5	1·2	1·7	54·3
54·6	1·1	1·4	1·1	1·4	1·1	1·4	1·2	1·5	1·3	1·6	1·4	1·7	1·5	1·8	54·6
54·9	1·4	1·6	1·5	1·6	1·5	1·6	1·6	1·7	1·6	1·8	1·8	1·9	1·9	2·0	54·9
55·2	1·8	1·8	1·8	1·8	1·9	1·9	1·9	1·9	2·0	2·0	2·1	2·1	2·2	2·2	55·2
55·5	2·2	2·0	2·2	2·0	2·3	2·1	2·3	2·1	2·4	2·2	2·4	2·3	2·5	2·4	55·5
55·8	2·6	2·2	2·6	2·2	2·6	2·3	2·7	2·3	2·7	2·4	2·8	2·4	2·9	2·5	55·8
56·1	3·0	2·4	3·0	2·5	3·0	2·5	3·0	2·5	3·1	2·6	3·1	2·6	3·2	2·7	56·1
56·4	3·4	2·7	3·4	2·7	3·4	2·7	3·4	2·7	3·4	2·8	3·5	2·8	3·5	2·9	56·4
56·7	3·7	2·9	3·7	2·9	3·8	2·9	3·8	2·9	3·8	3·0	3·8	3·0	3·9	3·0	56·7
57·0	4·1	3·1	4·1	3·1	4·1	3·1	4·1	3·1	4·2	3·1	4·2	3·2	4·2	3·2	57·0
57·3	4·5	3·3	4·5	3·3	4·5	3·3	4·5	3·3	4·5	3·3	4·5	3·4	4·6	3·4	57·3
57·6	4·9	3·5	4·9	3·5	4·9	3·5	4·9	3·5	4·9	3·5	4·9	3·5	4·9	3·6	57·6
57·9	5·3	3·8	5·3	3·8	5·2	3·8	5·2	3·7	5·2	3·7	5·2	3·7	5·2	3·7	57·9
58·2	5·6	4·0	5·6	4·0	5·6	4·0	5·6	4·0	5·6	3·9	5·6	3·9	5·6	3·9	58·2
58·5	6·0	4·2	6·0	4·2	6·0	4·2	6·0	4·2	6·0	4·1	5·9	4·1	5·9	4·1	58·5
58·8	6·4	4·4	6·4	4·4	6·4	4·4	6·3	4·4	6·3	4·3	6·3	4·3	6·2	4·2	58·8
59·1	6·8	4·6	6·8	4·6	6·7	4·6	6·7	4·6	6·7	4·5	6·6	4·5	6·6	4·4	59·1
59·4	7·2	4·8	7·1	4·8	7·1	4·8	7·1	4·8	7·0	4·7	7·0	4·7	6·9	4·6	59·4
59·7	7·5	5·1	7·5	5·0	7·5	5·0	7·5	5·0	7·4	4·9	7·3	4·8	7·2	4·7	59·7
60·0	7·9	5·3	7·9	5·3	7·9	5·2	7·8	5·2	7·8	5·1	7·7	5·0	7·6	4·9	60·0
60·3	8·3	5·5	8·3	5·5	8·2	5·4	8·2	5·4	8·1	5·3	8·0	5·2	7·9	5·1	60·3
60·6	8·7	5·7	8·7	5·7	8·6	5·7	8·6	5·6	8·5	5·5	8·4	5·4	8·2	5·3	60·6
60·9	9·1	5·9	9·0	5·9	9·0	5·9	8·9	5·8	8·8	5·7	8·7	5·6	8·6	5·4	60·9
61·2	9·5	6·2	9·4	6·1	9·4	6·1	9·3	6·0	9·2	5·9	9·1	5·8	8·9	5·6	61·2
61·5	9·8	6·4	9·8	6·3	9·7	6·3	9·7	6·2	9·5	6·1	9·4	5·9	9·2	5·8	61·5

DIP

Ht. of Eye	Corrn	Ht. of Eye	Ht. of Eye	Corrn	Ht. of Eye
m	′	ft.	m	′	ft.
2·4		8·0	9·5		31·5
	−2·8			−5·5	
2·6		8·6	9·9		32·7
	−2·9			−5·6	
2·8		9·2	10·3		33·9
	−3·0			−5·7	
3·0		9·8	10·6		35·1
	−3·1			−5·8	
3·2		10·5	11·0		36·3
	−3·2			−5·9	
3·4		11·2	11·4		37·6
	−3·3			−6·0	
3·6		11·9	11·8		38·9
	−3·4			−6·1	
3·8		12·6	12·2		40·1
	−3·5			−6·2	
4·0		13·3	12·6		41·5
	−3·6			−6·3	
4·3		14·1	13·0		42·8
	−3·7			−6·4	
4·5		14·9	13·4		44·2
	−3·8			−6·5	
4·7		15·7	13·8		45·5
	−3·9			−6·6	
5·0		16·5	14·2		46·9
	−4·0			−6·7	
5·2		17·4	14·7		48·4
	−4·1			−6·8	
5·5		18·3	15·1		49·8
	−4·2			−6·9	
5·8		19·1	15·5		51·3
	−4·3			−7·0	
6·1		20·1	16·0		52·8
	−4·4			−7·1	
6·3		21·0	16·5		54·3
	−4·5			−7·2	
6·6		22·0	16·9		55·8
	−4·6			−7·3	
6·9		22·9	17·4		57·4
	−4·7			−7·4	
7·2		23·9	17·9		58·9
	−4·8			−7·5	
7·5		24·9	18·4		60·5
	−4·9			−7·6	
7·9		26·0	18·8		62·1
	−5·0			−7·7	
8·2		27·1	19·3		63·8
	−5·1			−7·8	
8·5		28·1	19·8		65·4
	−5·2			−7·9	
8·8		29·2	20·4		67·1
	−5·3			−8·0	
9·2		30·4	20·9		68·8
	−5·4			−8·1	
9·5		31·5	21·4		70·5

MOON CORRECTION TABLE

The correction is in two parts; the first correction is taken from the upper part of the table with argument apparent altitude, and the second from the lower part, with argument H.P., in the same column as that from which the first correction was taken. Separate corrections are given in the lower part for lower (L) and upper (U) limbs. All corrections are to be **added** to apparent altitude, *but* 30′ *is to be subtracted from the altitude of the upper limb.*

For corrections for pressure and temperature see page A4.

For bubble sextant observations ignore dip, take the mean of upper and lower limb corrections and subtract 15′ from the altitude.

App. Alt. = Apparent altitude = Sextant altitude corrected for index error and dip.

CONVERSION OF ARC TO TIME

0°–59°		60°–119°		120°–179°		180°–239°		240°–299°		300°–359°			0'·00	0'·25	0'·50	0'·75
°	h m	°	h m	°	h m	°	h m	°	h m	°	h m	'	m s	m s	m s	m s
0	0 00	**60**	4 00	**120**	8 00	**180**	12 00	**240**	16 00	**300**	20 00	**0**	0 00	0 01	0 02	0 03
1	0 04	**61**	4 04	**121**	8 04	**181**	12 04	**241**	16 04	**301**	20 04	**1**	0 04	0 05	0 06	0 07
2	0 08	**62**	4 08	**122**	8 08	**182**	12 08	**242**	16 08	**302**	20 08	**2**	0 08	0 09	0 10	0 11
3	0 12	**63**	4 12	**123**	8 12	**183**	12 12	**243**	16 12	**303**	20 12	**3**	0 12	0 13	0 14	0 15
4	0 16	**64**	4 16	**124**	8 16	**184**	12 16	**244**	16 16	**304**	20 16	**4**	0 16	0 17	0 18	0 19
5	0 20	**65**	4 20	**125**	8 20	**185**	12 20	**245**	16 20	**305**	20 20	**5**	0 20	0 21	0 22	0 23
6	0 24	**66**	4 24	**126**	8 24	**186**	12 24	**246**	16 24	**306**	20 24	**6**	0 24	0 25	0 26	0 27
7	0 28	**67**	4 28	**127**	8 28	**187**	12 28	**247**	16 28	**307**	20 28	**7**	0 28	0 29	0 30	0 31
8	0 32	**68**	4 32	**128**	8 32	**188**	12 32	**248**	16 32	**308**	20 32	**8**	0 32	0 33	0 34	0 35
9	0 36	**69**	4 36	**129**	8 36	**189**	12 36	**249**	16 36	**309**	20 36	**9**	0 36	0 37	0 38	0 39
10	0 40	**70**	4 40	**130**	8 40	**190**	12 40	**250**	16 40	**310**	20 40	**10**	0 40	0 41	0 42	0 43
11	0 44	**71**	4 44	**131**	8 44	**191**	12 44	**251**	16 44	**311**	20 44	**11**	0 44	0 45	0 46	0 47
12	0 48	**72**	4 48	**132**	8 48	**192**	12 48	**252**	16 48	**312**	20 48	**12**	0 48	0 49	0 50	0 51
13	0 52	**73**	4 52	**133**	8 52	**193**	12 52	**253**	16 52	**313**	20 52	**13**	0 52	0 53	0 54	0 55
14	0 56	**74**	4 56	**134**	8 56	**194**	12 56	**254**	16 56	**314**	20 56	**14**	0 56	0 57	0 58	0 59
15	1 00	**75**	5 00	**135**	9 00	**195**	13 00	**255**	17 00	**315**	21 00	**15**	1 00	1 01	1 02	1 03
16	1 04	**76**	5 04	**136**	9 04	**196**	13 04	**256**	17 04	**316**	21 04	**16**	1 04	1 05	1 06	1 07
17	1 08	**77**	5 08	**137**	9 08	**197**	13 08	**257**	17 08	**317**	21 08	**17**	1 08	1 09	1 10	1 11
18	1 12	**78**	5 12	**138**	9 12	**198**	13 12	**258**	17 12	**318**	21 12	**18**	1 12	1 13	1 14	1 15
19	1 16	**79**	5 16	**139**	9 16	**199**	13 16	**259**	17 16	**319**	21 16	**19**	1 16	1 17	1 18	1 19
20	1 20	**80**	5 20	**140**	9 20	**200**	13 20	**260**	17 20	**320**	21 20	**20**	1 20	1 21	1 22	1 23
21	1 24	**81**	5 24	**141**	9 24	**201**	13 24	**261**	17 24	**321**	21 24	**21**	1 24	1 25	1 26	1 27
22	1 28	**82**	5 28	**142**	9 28	**202**	13 28	**262**	17 28	**322**	21 28	**22**	1 28	1 29	1 30	1 31
23	1 32	**83**	5 32	**143**	9 32	**203**	13 32	**263**	17 32	**323**	21 32	**23**	1 32	1 33	1 34	1 35
24	1 36	**84**	5 36	**144**	9 36	**204**	13 36	**264**	17 36	**324**	21 36	**24**	1 36	1 37	1 38	1 39
25	1 40	**85**	5 40	**145**	9 40	**205**	13 40	**265**	17 40	**325**	21 40	**25**	1 40	1 41	1 42	1 43
26	1 44	**86**	5 44	**146**	9 44	**206**	13 44	**266**	17 44	**326**	21 44	**26**	1 44	1 45	1 46	1 47
27	1 48	**87**	5 48	**147**	9 48	**207**	13 48	**267**	17 48	**327**	21 48	**27**	1 48	1 49	1 50	1 51
28	1 52	**88**	5 52	**148**	9 52	**208**	13 52	**268**	17 52	**328**	21 52	**28**	1 52	1 53	1 54	1 55
29	1 56	**89**	5 56	**149**	9 56	**209**	13 56	**269**	17 56	**329**	21 56	**29**	1 56	1 57	1 58	1 59
30	2 00	**90**	6 00	**150**	10 00	**210**	14 00	**270**	18 00	**330**	22 00	**30**	2 00	2 01	2 02	2 03
31	2 04	**91**	6 04	**151**	10 04	**211**	14 04	**271**	18 04	**331**	22 04	**31**	2 04	2 05	2 06	2 07
32	2 08	**92**	6 08	**152**	10 08	**212**	14 08	**272**	18 08	**332**	22 08	**32**	2 08	2 09	2 10	2 11
33	2 12	**93**	6 12	**153**	10 12	**213**	14 12	**273**	18 12	**333**	22 12	**33**	2 12	2 13	2 14	2 15
34	2 16	**94**	6 16	**154**	10 16	**214**	14 16	**274**	18 16	**334**	22 16	**34**	2 16	2 17	2 18	2 19
35	2 20	**95**	6 20	**155**	10 20	**215**	14 20	**275**	18 20	**335**	22 20	**35**	2 20	2 21	2 22	2 23
36	2 24	**96**	6 24	**156**	10 24	**216**	14 24	**276**	18 24	**336**	22 24	**36**	2 24	2 25	2 26	2 27
37	2 28	**97**	6 28	**157**	10 28	**217**	14 28	**277**	18 28	**337**	22 28	**37**	2 28	2 29	2 30	2 31
38	2 32	**98**	6 32	**158**	10 32	**218**	14 32	**278**	18 32	**338**	22 32	**38**	2 32	2 33	2 34	2 35
39	2 36	**99**	6 36	**159**	10 36	**219**	14 36	**279**	18 36	**339**	22 36	**39**	2 36	2 37	2 38	2 39
40	2 40	**100**	6 40	**160**	10 40	**220**	14 40	**280**	18 40	**340**	22 40	**40**	2 40	2 41	2 42	2 43
41	2 44	**101**	6 44	**161**	10 44	**221**	14 44	**281**	18 44	**341**	22 44	**41**	2 44	2 45	2 46	2 47
42	2 48	**102**	6 48	**162**	10 48	**222**	14 48	**282**	18 48	**342**	22 48	**42**	2 48	2 49	2 50	2 51
43	2 52	**103**	6 52	**163**	10 52	**223**	14 52	**283**	18 52	**343**	22 52	**43**	2 52	2 53	2 54	2 55
44	2 56	**104**	6 56	**164**	10 56	**224**	14 56	**284**	18 56	**344**	22 56	**44**	2 56	2 57	2 58	2 59
45	3 00	**105**	7 00	**165**	11 00	**225**	15 00	**285**	19 00	**345**	23 00	**45**	3 00	3 01	3 02	3 03
46	3 04	**106**	7 04	**166**	11 04	**226**	15 04	**286**	19 04	**346**	23 04	**46**	3 04	3 05	3 06	3 07
47	3 08	**107**	7 08	**167**	11 08	**227**	15 08	**287**	19 08	**347**	23 08	**47**	3 08	3 09	3 10	3 11
48	3 12	**108**	7 12	**168**	11 12	**228**	15 12	**288**	19 12	**348**	23 12	**48**	3 12	3 13	3 14	3 15
49	3 16	**109**	7 16	**169**	11 16	**229**	15 16	**289**	19 16	**349**	23 16	**49**	3 16	3 17	3 18	3 19
50	3 20	**110**	7 20	**170**	11 20	**230**	15 20	**290**	19 20	**350**	23 20	**50**	3 20	3 21	3 22	3 23
51	3 24	**111**	7 24	**171**	11 24	**231**	15 24	**291**	19 24	**351**	23 24	**51**	3 24	3 25	3 26	3 27
52	3 28	**112**	7 28	**172**	11 28	**232**	15 28	**292**	19 28	**352**	23 28	**52**	3 28	3 29	3 30	3 31
53	3 32	**113**	7 32	**173**	11 32	**233**	15 32	**293**	19 32	**353**	23 32	**53**	3 32	3 33	3 34	3 35
54	3 36	**114**	7 36	**174**	11 36	**234**	15 36	**294**	19 36	**354**	23 36	**54**	3 36	3 37	3 38	3 39
55	3 40	**115**	7 40	**175**	11 40	**235**	15 40	**295**	19 40	**355**	23 40	**55**	3 40	3 41	3 42	3 43
56	3 44	**116**	7 44	**176**	11 44	**236**	15 44	**296**	19 44	**356**	23 44	**56**	3 44	3 45	3 46	3 47
57	3 48	**117**	7 48	**177**	11 48	**237**	15 48	**297**	19 48	**357**	23 48	**57**	3 48	3 49	3 50	3 51
58	3 52	**118**	7 52	**178**	11 52	**238**	15 52	**298**	19 52	**358**	23 52	**58**	3 52	3 53	3 54	3 55
59	3 56	**119**	7 56	**179**	11 56	**239**	15 56	**299**	19 56	**359**	23 56	**59**	3 56	3 57	3 58	3 59

The above table is for converting expressions in arc to their equivalent in time ; its main use in this Almanac is for the conversion of longitude for application to L.M.T. (*added* if *west*, *subtracted* if *east*) to give G.M.T. or vice

T

POLARIS (POLE STAR) TABLES, 1983

FOR DETERMINING LATITUDE FROM SEXTANT ALTITUDE AND FOR AZIMUTH

L.H.A. ARIES	240°–249°	250°–259°	260°–269°	270°–279°	280°–289°	290°–299°	300°–309°	310°–319°	320°–329°	330°–339°	340°–349°	350°–359°
	a_0	a_0	a_0	a_0	a_0	a_0	a_0	a_0	a_0	a_0	a_0	a_0
°	° ′	° ′	° ′	° ′	° ′	° ′	° ′	° ′	° ′	° ′	° ′	° ′
0	1 42·4	1 38·1	1 32·6	1 26·0	1 18·7	1 10·7	1 02·3	0 53·8	0 45·5	0 37·6	0 30·3	0 23·8
1	42·1	37·6	32·0	25·3	17·9	09·8	01·5	53·0	44·7	36·8	29·6	23·3
2	41·7	37·1	31·3	24·6	17·1	09·0	1 00·6	52·2	43·9	36·1	28·9	22·7
3	41·3	36·6	30·7	23·9	16·3	08·2	0 59·8	51·3	43·1	35·3	28·2	22·1
4	40·9	36·0	30·1	23·2	15·5	07·4	58·9	50·5	42·3	34·6	27·6	21·6
5	1 40·4	1 35·5	1 29·4	1 22·4	1 14·7	1 06·5	0 58·1	0 49·6	0 41·5	0 33·8	0 26·9	0 21·0
6	40·0	34·9	28·8	21·7	13·9	05·7	57·2	48·8	40·7	33·1	26·3	20·5
7	39·5	34·3	28·1	20·9	13·1	04·8	56·4	48·0	39·9	32·4	25·7	20·0
8	39·1	33·8	27·4	20·2	12·3	04·0	55·5	47·2	39·1	31·7	25·0	19·5
9	38·6	33·2	26·7	19·4	11·5	03·2	54·7	46·3	38·3	31·0	24·4	19·0
10	1 38·1	1 32·6	1 26·0	1 18·7	1 10·7	1 02·3	0 53·8	0 45·5	0 37·6	0 30·3	0 23·8	0 18·5
Lat.	a_1	a_1	a_1	a_1	a_1	a_1	a_1	a_1	a_1	a_1	a_1	a_1
°	′	′	′	′	′	′	′	′	′	′	′	′
0	0·5	0·4	0·4	0·3	0·2	0·2	0·2	0·2	0·2	0·3	0·4	0·4
10	·5	·4	·4	·3	·3	·3	·3	·3	·3	·3	·4	·5
20	·5	·5	·4	·4	·3	·3	·3	·3	·4	·4	·4	·5
30	·5	·5	·5	·4	·4	·4	·4	·4	·4	·4	·5	·5
40	0·6	0·5	0·5	0·5	0·5	0·5	0·5	0·5	0·5	0·5	0·5	0·6
45	·6	·6	·6	·5	·5	·5	·5	·5	·5	·6	·6	·6
50	·6	·6	·6	·6	·6	·6	·6	·6	·6	·6	·6	·6
55	·6	·6	·6	·7	·7	·7	·7	·7	·7	·7	·6	·6
60	·7	·7	·7	·7	·8	·8	·8	·8	·8	·7	·7	·7
62	0·7	0·7	0·7	0·8	0·8	0·8	0·8	0·8	0·8	0·8	0·7	0·7
64	·7	·7	·8	·8	·9	0·9	0·9	·9	·9	·8	·8	·7
66	·7	·8	·8	·9	0·9	1·0	1·0	0·9	0·9	·9	·8	·7
68	0·7	0·8	0·9	0·9	1·0	1·0	1·0	1·0	1·0	0·9	0·8	0·8
Month	a_2	a_2	a_2	a_2	a_2	a_2	a_2	a_2	a_2	a_2	a_2	a_2
	′	′	′	′	′	′	′	′	′	′	′	′
Jan.	0·5	0·5	0·5	0·5	0·6	0·6	0·6	0·6	0·6	0·6	0·6	0·6
Feb.	·4	·4	·4	·4	·4	·4	·4	·4	·5	·5	·5	·6
Mar.	·4	·4	·4	·3	·3	·3	·3	·3	·3	·3	·4	·4
Apr.	0·5	0·5	0·4	0·4	0·3	0·3	0·2	0·2	0·2	0·2	0·2	0·3
May	·7	·6	·5	·4	·4	·3	·3	·2	·2	·2	·2	·2
June	·8	·7	·7	·6	·5	·4	·4	·3	·3	·2	·2	·2
July	0·9	0·9	0·8	0·7	0·7	0·6	0·5	0·5	0·4	0·3	0·3	0·2
Aug.	1·0	·9	·9	·9	·8	·8	·7	·6	·6	·5	·4	·4
Sept.	0·9	·9	·9	·9	·9	·9	·8	·8	·7	·7	·6	·6
Oct.	0·8	0·9	0·9	0·9	0·9	0·9	0·9	0·9	0·9	0·8	0·8	0·8
Nov.	·7	·7	·8	·8	·9	·9	·9	1·0	1·0	1·0	0·9	0·9
Dec.	0·5	0·6	0·6	0·7	0·8	0·8	0·9	0·9	1·0	1·0	1·0	1·0
Lat.						AZIMUTH						
°	°	°	°	°	°	°	°	°	°	°	°	°
0	0·4	0·5	0·6	0·7	0·8	0·8	0·8	0·8	0·8	0·7	0·6	0·5
20	0·4	0·6	0·7	0·8	0·8	0·9	0·9	0·8	0·8	0·7	0·6	0·5
40	0·5	0·7	0·8	0·9	1·0	1·0	1·1	1·0	1·0	0·9	0·8	0·7
50	0·6	0·8	1·0	1·1	1·2	1·2	1·3	1·2	1·2	1·1	1·0	0·8
55	0·7	0·9	1·1	1·2	1·3	1·4	1·4	1·4	1·3	1·2	1·1	0·9
60	0·8	1·1	1·2	1·4	1·5	1·6	1·6	1·6	1·5	1·4	1·2	1·0
65	1·0	1·2	1·5	1·7	1·8	1·9	1·9	1·9	1·8	1·7	1·5	1·2

Latitude = Apparent altitude (corrected for refraction) $- 1° + a_0 + a_1 + a_2$

The table is entered with L.H.A. Aries to determine the column to be used; each column refers to a range of 10°. a_0 is taken, with mental interpolation, from the upper table with the units of L.H.A. Aries in degrees as argument; a_1, a_2 are taken, without interpolation, from the second and third tables with arguments latitude and month respectively. a_0, a_1, a_2 are always positive. The final table gives the azimuth of *Polaris*.

1983 JANUARY 22, 23, 24 (SAT., SUN., MON.)

G.M.T.		SUN G.H.A.	SUN Dec.	MOON G.H.A.	MOON *v*	MOON Dec.	MOON *d*	MOON H.P.
d	h	° ′	° ′	° ′	′	° ′	′	′
22	00	177 09.2	S19 51.2	92 30.9	13.1	N 6 31.0	12.6	57.0
	01	192 09.0	50.6	107 03.0	13.1	6 43.6	12.6	57.0
	02	207 08.9	50.0	121 35.1	13.0	6 56.2	12.6	57.0
	03	222 08.7	·· 49.5	136 07.1	13.0	7 08.8	12.6	57.1
	04	237 08.5	48.9	150 39.1	12.9	7 21.4	12.5	57.1
	05	252 08.3	48.4	165 11.0	12.8	7 33.9	12.6	57.1
	06	267 08.2	S19 47.8	179 42.8	12.7	N 7 46.5	12.5	57.2
	07	282 08.0	47.2	194 14.5	12.7	7 59.0	12.5	57.2
S	08	297 07.8	46.7	208 46.2	12.6	8 11.5	12.4	57.3
A	09	312 07.7	·· 46.1	223 17.8	12.5	8 23.9	12.5	57.3
T	10	327 07.5	45.5	237 49.3	12.5	8 36.4	12.4	57.3
U	11	342 07.3	45.0	252 20.8	12.4	8 48.8	12.4	57.4
R	12	357 07.1	S19 44.4	266 52.2	12.3	N 9 01.2	12.4	57.4
D	13	12 07.0	43.8	281 23.5	12.2	9 13.6	12.3	57.4
A	14	27 06.8	43.3	295 54.7	12.2	9 25.9	12.3	57.5
Y	15	42 06.6	·· 42.7	310 25.9	12.1	9 38.2	12.3	57.5
	16	57 06.5	42.1	324 57.0	12.0	9 50.5	12.2	57.5
	17	72 06.3	41.5	339 28.0	11.9	10 02.7	12.2	57.6
	18	87 06.1	S19 41.0	353 58.9	11.8	N10 14.9	12.2	57.6
	19	102 06.0	40.4	8 29.7	11.8	10 27.1	12.1	57.7
	20	117 05.8	39.8	23 00.5	11.7	10 39.2	12.1	57.7
	21	132 05.6	·· 39.3	37 31.2	11.6	10 51.3	12.1	57.7
	22	147 05.5	38.7	52 01.8	11.5	11 03.4	12.0	57.8
	23	162 05.3	38.1	66 32.3	11.4	11 15.4	12.0	57.8
23	00	177 05.1	S19 37.5	81 02.7	11.3	N11 27.4	11.9	57.8
	01	192 05.0	37.0	95 33.0	11.2	11 39.3	11.9	57.9
	02	207 04.8	36.4	110 03.2	11.2	11 51.2	11.9	57.9
	03	222 04.6	·· 35.8	124 33.4	11.0	12 03.1	11.8	58.0
	04	237 04.5	35.2	139 03.4	11.0	12 14.9	11.7	58.0
	05	252 04.3	34.6	153 33.4	10.9	12 26.6	11.7	58.0
	06	267 04.1	S19 34.1	168 03.3	10.8	N12 38.3	11.7	58.1
	07	282 04.0	33.5	182 33.1	10.6	12 50.0	11.6	58.1
	08	297 03.8	32.9	197 02.7	10.6	13 01.6	11.5	58.1
S	09	312 03.7	·· 32.3	211 32.3	10.5	13 13.1	11.5	58.2
U	10	327 03.5	31.7	226 01.8	10.4	13 24.6	11.4	58.2
N	11	342 03.3	31.2	240 31.2	10.3	13 36.0	11.4	58.3
D	12	357 03.2	S19 30.6	255 00.5	10.2	N13 47.4	11.3	58.3
A	13	12 03.0	30.0	269 29.7	10.1	13 58.7	11.3	58.3
Y	14	27 02.8	29.4	283 58.8	10.0	14 10.0	11.2	58.4
	15	42 02.7	·· 28.8	298 27.8	9.9	14 21.2	11.1	58.4
	16	57 02.5	28.2	312 56.7	9.8	14 32.3	11.1	58.5
	17	72 02.4	27.7	327 25.5	9.7	14 43.4	11.0	58.5
	18	87 02.2	S19 27.1	341 54.2	9.6	N14 54.4	11.0	58.5
	19	102 02.0	26.5	356 22.8	9.5	15 05.4	10.8	58.6
	20	117 01.9	25.9	10 51.3	9.3	15 16.2	10.8	58.6
	21	132 01.7	·· 25.3	25 19.6	9.3	15 27.0	10.7	58.6
	22	147 01.6	24.7	39 47.9	9.2	15 37.7	10.7	58.7
	23	162 01.4	24.1	54 16.1	9.0	15 48.4	10.6	58.7
24	00	177 01.3	S19 23.5	68 44.1	9.0	N15 59.0	10.5	58.8
	01	192 01.1	23.0	83 12.1	8.8	16 09.5	10.4	58.8
	02	207 00.9	22.4	97 39.9	8.8	16 19.9	10.3	58.8
	03	222 00.8	·· 21.8	112 07.7	8.6	16 30.2	10.3	58.9
	04	237 00.6	21.2	126 35.3	8.5	16 40.5	10.1	58.9
	05	252 00.5	20.6	141 02.8	8.4	16 50.6	10.1	59.0
	06	267 00.3	S19 20.0	155 30.2	8.3	N17 00.7	10.0	59.0
	07	282 00.2	19.4	169 57.5	8.2	17 10.7	9.9	59.0
	08	297 00.0	18.8	184 24.7	8.1	17 20.6	9.9	59.1
M	09	311 59.9	·· 18.2	198 51.8	7.9	17 30.5	9.7	59.1
O	10	326 59.7	17.6	213 18.7	7.9	17 40.2	9.6	59.1
N	11	341 59.5	17.0	227 45.6	7.7	17 49.8	9.6	59.2
D	12	356 59.4	S19 16.4	242 12.3	7.7	N17 59.4	9.4	59.2
A	13	11 59.2	15.8	256 39.0	7.5	18 08.8	9.4	59.3
Y	14	26 59.1	15.2	271 05.5	7.4	18 18.2	9.2	59.3
	15	41 58.9	·· 14.6	285 31.9	7.3	18 27.4	9.2	59.3
	16	56 58.8	14.0	299 58.2	7.2	18 36.6	9.0	59.4
	17	71 58.6	13.4	314 24.4	7.0	18 45.6	8.9	59.4
	18	86 58.5	S19 12.8	328 50.4	7.0	N18 54.5	8.9	59.4
	19	101 58,3	12.2	343 16.4	6.8	19 03.4	8.7	59.5
	20	116 58.2	11.6	357 42.2	6.7	19 12.1	8.6	59.5
	21	131 58.0	·· 11.0	12 07.9	6.7	19 20.7	8.5	59.6
	22	146 57.9	10.4	26 33.6	6.5	19 29.2	8.4	59.6
	23	161 57.7	09.8	40 59.1	6.4	19 37.6	8.2	59.6
		S.D. 16.3	*d* 0.6	S.D. 15.6		15.9		16.1

Lat.	Twilight Naut.	Twilight Civil	Sunrise	Moonrise 22	Moonrise 23	Moonrise 24	Moonrise 25
°	h m	h m	h m	h m	h m	h m	h m
N 72	07 41	09 20	■	10 19	09 50	08 49	□
N 70	07 29	08 54	10 45	10 32	10 14	09 47	□
68	07 19	08 34	09 59	10 42	10 33	10 21	09 59
66	07 11	08 18	09 29	10 50	10 48	10 46	10 46
64	07 04	08 05	09 07	10 58	11 00	11 06	11 17
62	06 57	07 54	08 49	11 04	11 11	11 22	11 40
60	06 52	07 44	08 35	11 09	11 20	11 36	11 59
N 58	06 47	07 36	08 22	11 14	11 28	11 47	12 15
56	06 42	07 28	08 11	11 19	11 35	11 57	12 28
54	06 38	07 22	08 02	11 23	11 42	12 06	12 40
52	06 34	07 15	07 53	11 26	11 48	12 14	12 50
50	06 30	07 10	07 46	11 29	11 53	12 22	12 59
45	06 22	06 58	07 30	11 36	12 04	12 37	13 19
N 40	06 14	06 47	07 16	11 42	12 14	12 50	13 34
35	06 07	06 38	07 05	11 47	12 22	13 01	13 48
30	06 00	06 29	06 55	11 52	12 29	13 11	14 00
20	05 48	06 14	06 38	12 00	12 41	13 28	14 20
N 10	05 35	06 00	06 22	12 07	12 52	13 42	14 38
0	05 21	05 46	06 08	12 13	13 03	13 56	14 54
S 10	05 05	05 31	05 54	12 20	13 13	14 10	15 11
20	04 46	05 14	05 38	12 27	13 24	14 25	15 29
30	04 22	04 54	05 20	12 36	13 37	14 42	15 50
35	04 07	04 41	05 10	12 40	13 45	14 52	16 02
40	03 48	04 26	04 57	12 46	13 53	15 04	16 16
45	03 24	04 08	04 43	12 52	14 04	15 18	16 33
S 50	02 51	03 45	04 25	13 00	14 16	15 35	16 53
52	02 34	03 34	04 17	13 03	14 22	15 42	17 03
54	02 12	03 21	04 07	13 07	14 28	15 51	17 14
56	01 42	03 05	03 57	13 12	14 35	16 01	17 27
58	00 49	02 47	03 45	13 17	14 43	16 13	17 42
S 60	////	02 24	03 30	13 22	14 52	16 26	17 59

Lat.	Sunset	Twilight Civil	Twilight Naut.	Moonset 22	Moonset 23	Moonset 24	Moonset 25
°	h m	h m	h m	h m	h m	h m	h m
N 72	■	15 04	16 44	01 16	03 26	06 16	□
N 70	13 40	15 30	16 56	01 06	03 04	05 20	□
68	14 26	15 50	17 05	00 58	02 47	04 46	07 07
66	14 55	16 06	17 14	00 51	02 33	04 22	06 20
64	15 17	16 19	17 21	00 46	02 22	04 04	05 50
62	15 35	16 30	17 27	00 41	02 12	03 48	05 28
60	15 50	16 40	17 32	00 37	02 04	03 36	05 09
N 58	16 02	16 48	17 38	00 33	01 57	03 25	04 54
56	16 13	16 56	17 42	00 30	01 51	03 15	04 42
54	16 22	17 03	17 46	00 27	01 45	03 07	04 30
52	16 31	17 09	17 50	00 24	01 40	03 00	04 21
50	16 38	17 14	17 54	00 21	01 36	02 53	04 12
45	16 54	17 27	18 02	00 16	01 26	02 38	03 53
N 40	17 08	17 37	18 10	00 12	01 18	02 27	03 38
35	17 19	17 46	18 17	00 08	01 11	02 17	03 25
30	17 29	17 54	18 23	00 05	01 05	02 08	03 14
20	17 46	18 09	18 36	24 54	00 54	01 53	02 55
N 10	18 01	18 23	18 49	24 45	00 45	01 40	02 39
0	18 15	18 37	19 03	24 36	00 36	01 28	02 23
S 10	18 30	18 52	19 18	24 28	00 28	01 15	02 08
20	18 45	19 09	19 37	24 19	00 19	01 02	01 51
30	19 03	19 29	20 01	24 09	00 09	00 48	01 33
35	19 14	19 42	20 16	24 03	00 03	00 39	01 22
40	19 26	19 56	20 35	23 56	24 29	00 29	01 09
45	19 40	20 14	20 58	23 48	24 18	00 18	00 55
S 50	19 57	20 37	21 31	23 39	24 04	00 04	00 37
52	20 06	20 48	21 48	23 34	23 58	24 28	00 28
54	20 15	21 01	22 09	23 30	23 51	24 19	00 19
56	20 25	21 16	22 38	23 24	23 43	24 08	00 08
58	20 37	21 34	23 25	23 19	23 34	23 56	24 30
S 60	20 52	21 57	////	23 12	23 24	23 42	24 12

Day	SUN Eqn. of Time 00ʰ	SUN Eqn. of Time 12ʰ	SUN Mer. Pass.	MOON Mer. Pass. Upper	MOON Mer. Pass. Lower	MOON Age	MOON Phase
	m s	m s	h m	h m	h m	d	
22	11 23	11 31	12 12	18 25	06 01	08	◐
23	11 39	11 47	12 12	19 15	06 49	09	
24	11 55	12 02	12 12	20 10	07 42	10	

1983 JUNE 12, 13, 14 (SUN., MON., TUES.)

G.M.T. d	h	ARIES G.H.A.	VENUS −3.9 G.H.A.	VENUS Dec.	MARS +1.7 G.H.A.	MARS Dec.	JUPITER −2.1 G.H.A.	JUPITER Dec.	SATURN +0.7 G.H.A.	SATURN Dec.
		° ′	° ′	° ′	° ′	° ′	° ′	° ′	° ′	° ′
12	00	259 45.2	131 01.3	N21 00.7	182 36.6	N23 25.7	17 22.8	S20 07.6	52 46.2	S 8 19.1
	01	274 47.7	146 01.2	21 00.0	197 37.2	25.9	32 25.6	07.6	67 48.8	19.1
	02	289 50.1	161 01.2	20 59.3	212 37.8	26.1	47 28.3	07.5	82 51.3	19.1
	03	304 52.6	176 01.1	·· 58.6	227 38.4	·· 26.2	62 31.1	·· 07.5	97 53.9	·· 19.0
	04	319 55.1	191 01.0	57.9	242 39.0	26.4	77 33.9	07.4	112 56.4	19.0
	05	334 57.5	206 01.0	57.1	257 39.6	26.6	92 36.7	07.4	127 58.9	19.0
	06	350 00.0	221 00.9	N20 56.4	272 40.2	N23 26.8	107 39.4	S20 07.3	143 01.5	S 8 19.0
	07	5 02.5	236 00.9	55.7	287 40.8	26.9	122 42.2	07.3	158 04.0	19.0
	08	20 04.9	251 00.8	55.0	302 41.4	27.1	137 45.0	07.2	173 06.6	18.9
S	09	35 07.4	266 00.8	·· 54.3	317 42.0	·· 27.3	152 47.8	·· 07.2	188 09.1	·· 18.9
U	10	50 09.9	281 00.7	53.5	332 42.6	27.4	167 50.5	07.1	203 11.6	18.9
N	11	65 12.3	296 00.7	52.8	347 43.2	27.6	182 53.3	07.1	218 14.2	18.9
D	12	80 14.8	311 00.6	N20 52.1	2 43.8	N23 27.8	197 56.1	S20 07.0	233 16.7	S 8 18.9
A	13	95 17.2	326 00.6	51.4	17 44.4	28.0	212 58.8	07.0	248 19.3	18.9
Y	14	110 19.7	341 00.5	50.6	32 45.0	28.1	228 01.6	06.9	263 21.8	18.8
	15	125 22.2	356 00.5	·· 49.9	47 45.6	·· 28.3	243 04.4	·· 06.9	278 24.3	·· 18.8
	16	140 24.6	11 00.4	49.2	62 46.2	28.5	258 07.2	06.8	293 26.9	18.8
	17	155 27.1	26 00.4	48.4	77 46.8	28.6	273 09.9	06.8	308 29.4	18.8
	18	170 29.6	41 00.3	N20 47.7	92 47.4	N23 28.8	288 12.7	S20 06.8	323 32.0	S 8 18.8
	19	185 32.0	56 00.3	47.0	107 48.0	29.0	303 15.5	06.7	338 34.5	18.7
	20	200 34.5	71 00.2	46.3	122 48.6	29.1	318 18.2	06.7	353 37.0	18.7
	21	215 37.0	86 00.2	·· 45.5	137 49.2	·· 29.3	333 21.0	·· 06.6	8 39.6	·· 18.7
	22	230 39.4	101 00.2	44.8	152 49.8	29.5	348 23.8	06.6	23 42.1	18.7
	23	245 41.9	116 00.1	44.1	167 50.4	29.6	3 26.6	06.5	38 44.7	18.7
13	00	260 44.4	131 00.1	N20 43.3	182 51.0	N23 29.8	18 29.3	S20 06.5	53 47.2	S 8 18.7
	01	275 46.8	146 00.0	42.6	197 51.6	30.0	33 32.1	06.4	68 49.7	18.6
	02	290 49.3	161 00.0	41.9	212 52.2	30.1	48 34.9	06.4	83 52.3	18.6
	03	305 51.7	176 00.0	·· 41.1	227 52.8	·· 30.3	63 37.6	·· 06.3	98 54.8	·· 18.6
	04	320 54.2	190 59.9	40.4	242 53.4	30.5	78 40.4	06.3	113 57.3	18.6
	05	335 56.7	205 59.9	39.7	257 54.0	30.6	93 43.2	06.2	128 59.9	18.6
	06	350 59.1	220 59.9	N20 38.9	272 54.6	N23 30.8	108 45.9	S20 06.2	144 02.4	S 8 18.6
	07	6 01.6	235 59.9	38.2	287 55.2	31.0	123 48.7	06.1	159 05.0	18.5
	08	21 04.1	250 59.8	37.4	302 55.8	31.1	138 51.5	06.1	174 07.5	18.5
M	09	36 06.5	265 59.8	·· 36.7	317 56.4	·· 31.3	153 54.3	·· 06.0	189 10.0	·· 18.5
O	10	51 09.0	280 59.8	36.0	332 57.0	31.4	168 57.0	06.0	204 12.6	18.5
N	11	66 11.5	295 59.7	35.2	347 57.6	31.6	183 59.8	06.0	219 15.1	18.5
D	12	81 13.9	310 59.7	N20 34.5	2 58.2	N23 31.8	199 02.6	S20 05.9	234 17.6	S 8 18.5
A	13	96 16.4	325 59.7	33.7	17 58.8	31.9	214 05.3	05.9	249 20.2	18.4
Y	14	111 18.8	340 59.7	33.0	32 59.4	32.1	229 08.1	05.8	264 22.7	18.4
	15	126 21.3	355 59.7	·· 32.3	48 00.0	·· 32.3	244 10.9	·· 05.8	279 25.2	·· 18.4
	16	141 23.8	10 59.6	31.5	63 00.6	32.4	259 13.6	05.7	294 27.8	18.4
	17	156 26.2	25 59.6	30.8	78 01.2	32.6	274 16.4	05.7	309 30.3	18.4
	18	171 28.7	40 59.6	N20 30.0	93 01.8	N23 32.7	289 19.2	S20 05.6	324 32.8	S 8 18.4
	19	186 31.2	55 59.6	29.3	108 02.4	32.9	304 21.9	05.6	339 35.4	18.4
	20	201 33.6	70 59.6	28.5	123 03.0	33.0	319 24.7	05.5	354 37.9	18.3
	21	216 36.1	85 59.6	·· 27.8	138 03.6	·· 33.2	334 27.5	·· 05.5	9 40.5	·· 18.3
	22	231 38.6	100 59.6	27.0	153 04.2	33.4	349 30.2	05.4	24 43.0	18.3
	23	246 41.0	115 59.5	26.3	168 04.8	33.5	4 33.0	05.4	39 45.5	18.3
14	00	261 43.5	130 59.5	N20 25.6	183 05.4	N23 33.7	19 35.8	S20 05.3	54 48.1	S 8 18.3
	01	276 46.0	145 59.5	24.8	198 06.0	33.8	34 38.5	05.3	69 50.6	18.3
	02	291 48.4	160 59.5	24.1	213 06.6	34.0	49 41.3	05.2	84 53.1	18.2
	03	306 50.9	175 59.5	·· 23.3	228 07.2	·· 34.1	64 44.1	·· 05.2	99 55.7	·· 18.2
	04	321 53.3	190 59.5	22.6	243 07.8	34.3	79 46.8	05.2	114 58.2	18.2
	05	336 55.8	205 59.5	21.8	258 08.4	34.5	94 49.6	05.1	130 00.7	18.2
	06	351 58.3	220 59.5	N20 21.1	273 09.0	N23 34.6	109 52.4	S20 05.1	145 03.3	S 8 18.2
	07	7 00.7	235 59.5	20.3	288 09.6	34.8	124 55.1	05.0	160 05.8	18.2
T	08	22 03.2	250 59.5	19.6	303 10.2	34.9	139 57.9	05.0	175 08.3	18.2
U	09	37 05.7	265 59.5	·· 18.8	318 10.8	·· 35.1	155 00.7	·· 04.9	190 10.9	·· 18.1
E	10	52 08.1	280 59.5	18.0	333 11.4	35.2	170 03.4	04.9	205 13.4	18.1
S	11	67 10.6	295 59.5	17.3	348 12.0	35.4	185 06.2	04.8	220 15.9	18.1
D	12	82 13.1	310 59.5	N20 16.5	3 12.6	N23 35.5	200 09.0	S20 04.8	235 18.5	S 8 18.1
A	13	97 15.5	325 59.5	15.8	18 13.2	35.7	215 11.7	04.7	250 21.0	18.1
Y	14	112 18.0	340 59.5	15.0	33 13.8	35.8	230 14.5	04.7	265 23.5	18.1
	15	127 20.5	355 59.5	·· 14.3	48 14.4	·· 36.0	245 17.3	·· 04.6	280 26.1	·· 18.0
	16	142 22.9	10 59.6	13.5	63 15.0	36.1	260 20.0	04.6	295 28.6	18.0
	17	157 25.4	25 59.6	12.8	78 15.6	36.3	275 22.8	04.6	310 31.1	18.0
	18	172 27.8	40 59.6	N20 12.0	93 16.2	N23 36.4	290 25.6	S20 04.5	325 33.6	S 8 18.0
	19	187 30.3	55 59.6	11.2	108 16.8	36.6	305 28.3	04.5	340 36.2	18.0
	20	202 32.8	70 59.6	10.5	123 17.4	36.7	320 31.1	04.4	355 38.7	18.0
	21	217 35.2	85 59.6	·· 09.7	138 18.0	·· 36.9	335 33.8	·· 04.4	10 41.2	·· 18.0
	22	232 37.7	100 59.6	09.0	153 18.6	37.0	350 36.6	04.3	25 43.8	17.9
	23	247 40.2	115 59.7	08.2	168 19.2	37.2	5 39.4	04.3	40 46.3	17.9
Mer. Pass.		h m 6 36.0	*v* 0.0	*d* 0.7	*v* 0.6	*d* 0.2	*v* 2.8	*d* 0.0	*v* 2.5	*d* 0.0

STARS

Name	S.H.A. ° ′	Dec. ° ′
Acamar	315 36.1	S40 22.2
Achernar	335 44.0	S57 19.1
Acrux	173 35.0	S63 00.6
Adhara	255 30.9	S28 57.0
Aldebaran	291 16.1	N16 28.5
Alioth	166 40.5	N56 03.3
Alkaid	153 16.6	N49 24.0
Al Na'ir	28 12.2	S47 02.4
Alnilam	276 10.0	S 1 12.7
Alphard	218 18.8	S 8 35.2
Alphecca	126 30.1	N26 46.3
Alpheratz	358 07.4	N28 59.7
Altair	62 30.3	N 8 49.3
Ankaa	353 38.3	S42 23.7
Antares	112 54.1	S26 23.8
Arcturus	146 16.4	N19 16.2
Atria	108 16.1	S69 00.0
Avior	234 28.0	S59 27.5
Bellatrix	278 57.0	N 6 20.1
Betelgeuse	271 26.5	N 7 24.3
Canopus	264 06.9	S52 41.2
Capella	281 08.9	N45 58.9
Deneb	49 46.9	N45 13.0
Denebola	182 57.0	N14 40.1
Diphda	349 19.0	S18 04.7
Dubhe	194 19.7	N61 50.8
Elnath	278 42.1	N28 35.6
Eltanin	90 56.3	N51 29.4
Enif	34 09.5	N 9 47.8
Fomalhaut	15 49.2	S29 42.6
Gacrux	172 26.5	S57 01.4
Gienah	176 15.9	S17 27.0
Hadar	149 20.3	S60 17.8
Hamal	328 27.0	N23 22.9
Kaus Aust.	84 13.8	S34 23.6
Kochab	137 17.9	N74 13.7
Markab	14 01.2	N15 06.7
Menkar	314 39.4	N 4 01.4
Menkent	148 34.5	S36 17.4
Miaplacidus	221 45.2	S69 39.1
Mirfak	309 13.8	N49 48.0
Nunki	76 26.4	S26 19.1
Peacock	53 54.8	S56 47.2
Pollux	243 56.1	N28 04.2
Procyon	245 24.0	N 5 16.1
Rasalhague	96 27.4	N12 34.3
Regulus	208 08.0	N12 03.1
Rigel	281 34.5	S 8 13.2
Rigil Kent.	140 22.8	S60 46.1
Sabik	102 38.5	S15 42.3
Schedar	350 07.1	N56 26.4
Shaula	96 52.7	S37 05.6
Sirius	258 54.3	S16 41.6
Spica	158 55.3	S11 04.5
Suhail	223 09.7	S43 22.0
Vega	80 54.1	N38 46.0
Zuben'ubi	137 30.6	S15 58.4

	S.H.A. ° ′	Mer. Pass. h m
Venus	230 15.7	15 16
Mars	282 06.6	11 48
Jupiter	117 45.0	22 42
Saturn	153 02.8	20 21

1983 JUNE 12, 13, 14 (SUN., MON., TUES.)

	G.M.T.	SUN G.H.A.	SUN Dec.	MOON G.H.A.	v	MOON Dec.	d	H.P.
	d h	° ′	° ′	° ′	′	° ′	′	′
	12 00	180 06.4	N23 06.0	168 06.3	3.2	N24 01.6	2.8	60.3
	01	195 06.3	06.2	182 28.5	3.2	24 04.4	2.7	60.3
	02	210 06.2	06.3	196 50.7	3.1	24 07.1	2.6	60.3
	03	225 06.0	·· 06.5	211 12.8	3.1	24 09.7	2.3	60.3
	04	240 05.9	06.7	225 34.9	3.1	24 12.0	2.2	60.3
	05	255 05.8	06.8	239 57.0	3.0	24 14.2	1.9	60.3
	06	270 05.6	N23 07.0	254 19.0	3.0	N24 16.1	1.9	60.4
	07	285 05.5	07.2	268 41.0	2.9	24 18.0	1.6	60.4
	08	300 05.4	07.3	283 02.9	2.9	24 19.6	1.4	60.4
S	09	315 05.3	·· 07.5	297 24.8	2.9	24 21.0	1.3	60.4
U	10	330 05.1	07.7	311 46.7	2.9	24 22.3	1.1	60.4
N	11	345 05.0	07.8	326 08.6	2.9	24 23.4	0.9	60.4
D	12	0 04.9	N23 08.0	340 30.5	2.8	N24 24.3	0.8	60.4
A	13	15 04.7	08.2	354 52.3	2.9	24 25.1	0.5	60.4
Y	14	30 04.6	08.3	9 14.2	2.8	24 25.6	0.4	60.4
	15	45 04.5	·· 08.5	23 36.0	2.8	24 26.0	0.2	60.4
	16	60 04.3	08.6	37 57.8	2.8	24 26.2	0.0	60.4
	17	75 04.2	08.8	52 19.6	2.8	24 26.2	0.2	60.4
	18	90 04.1	N23 09.0	66 41.4	2.8	N24 26.0	0.3	60.5
	19	105 04.0	09.1	81 03.2	2.8	24 25.7	0.6	60.5
	20	120 03.8	09.3	95 25.0	2.7	24 25.1	0.7	60.5
	21	135 03.7	·· 09.4	109 46.7	2.9	24 24.4	0.9	60.5
	22	150 03.6	09.6	124 08.6	2.8	24 23.5	1.1	60.5
	23	165 03.4	09.7	138 30.4	2.8	24 22.4	1.2	60.5
	13 00	180 03.3	N23 09.9	152 52.2	2.8	N24 21.2	1.5	60.5
	01	195 03.2	10.0	167 14.0	2.9	24 19.7	1.6	60.5
	02	210 03.0	10.2	181 35.9	2.8	24 18.1	1.8	60.5
	03	225 02.9	·· 10.4	195 57.7	2.9	24 16.3	2.0	60.5
	04	240 02.8	10.5	210 19.6	2.9	24 14.3	2.1	60.5
	05	255 02.7	10.7	224 41.5	3.0	24 12.2	2.4	60.5
	06	270 02.5	N23 10.8	239 03.5	2.9	N24 09.8	2.5	60.5
	07	285 02.4	11.0	253 25.4	3.0	24 07.3	2.7	60.5
	08	300 02.3	11.1	267 47.4	3.0	24 04.6	2.8	60.5
M	09	315 02.1	·· 11.3	282 09.4	3.1	24 01.8	3.1	60.5
O	10	330 02.0	11.4	296 31.5	3.1	23 58.7	3.2	60.5
N	11	345 01.9	11.5	310 53.6	3.2	23 55.5	3.4	60.5
D	12	0 01.7	N23 11.7	325 15.8	3.1	N23 52.1	3.6	60.5
A	13	15 01.6	11.8	339 37.9	3.3	23 48.5	3.7	60.5
Y	14	30 01.5	12.0	354 00.2	3.2	23 44.8	3.9	60.5
	15	45 01.4	·· 12.1	8 22.4	3.4	23 40.9	4.1	60.5
	16	60 01.2	12.3	22 44.8	3.3	23 36.8	4.3	60.5
	17	75 01.1	12.4	37 07.1	3.5	23 32.5	4.4	60.5
	18	90 01.0	N23 12.5	51 29.6	3.4	N23 28.1	4.6	60.5
	19	105 00.8	12.7	65 52.0	3.6	23 23.5	4.8	60.4
	20	120 00.7	12.8	80 14.6	3.6	23 18.7	4.9	60.4
	21	135 00.6	·· 13.0	94 37.2	3.6	23 13.8	5.1	60.4
	22	150 00.4	13.1	108 59.8	3.7	23 08.7	5.3	60.4
	23	165 00.3	13.2	123 22.5	3.8	23 03.4	5.4	60.4
	14 00	180 00.2	N23 13.4	137 45.3	3.9	N22 58.0	5.6	60.4
	01	195 00.0	13.5	152 08.2	3.9	22 52.4	5.7	60.4
	02	209 59.9	13.7	166 31.1	4.0	22 46.7	5.9	60.4
	03	224 59.8	·· 13.8	180 54.1	4.0	22 40.8	6.1	60.4
	04	239 59.6	13.9	195 17.1	4.2	22 34.7	6.2	60.4
	05	254 59.5	14.1	209 40.3	4.2	22 28.5	6.4	60.4
	06	269 59.4	N23 14.2	224 03.5	4.3	N22 22.1	6.6	60.4
	07	284 59.2	14.3	238 26.8	4.3	22 15.5	6.7	60.4
	08	299 59.1	14.5	252 50.1	4.5	22 08.8	6.8	60.3
T	09	314 59.0	·· 14.6	267 13.6	4.5	22 02.0	7.0	60.3
U	10	329 58.8	14.7	281 37.1	4.6	21 55.0	7.1	60.3
E	11	344 58.7	14.8	296 00.7	4.7	21 47.9	7.3	60.3
S	12	359 58.6	N23 15.0	310 24.4	4.7	N21 40.6	7.5	60.3
D	13	14 58.4	15.1	324 48.1	4.9	21 33.1	7.6	60.3
A	14	29 58.3	15.2	339 12.0	4.9	21 25.5	7.7	60.3
Y	15	44 58.2	·· 15.4	353 35.9	5.0	21 17.8	7.9	60.3
	16	59 58.1	15.5	7 59.9	5.2	21 09.9	8.0	60.2
	17	74 57.9	15.6	22 24.1	5.2	21 01.9	8.1	60.2
	18	89 57.8	N23 15.7	36 48.3	5.2	N20 53.8	8.3	60.2
	19	104 57.7	15.9	51 12.5	5.4	20 45.5	8.4	60.2
	20	119 57.5	16.0	65 36.9	5.5	20 37.1	8.6	60.2
	21	134 57.4	·· 16.1	80 01.4	5.6	20 28.5	8.7	60.2
	22	149 57.3	16.2	94 26.0	5.6	20 19.8	8.8	60.2
	23	164 57.1	16.3	108 50.6	5.8	20 11.0	8.9	60.1
		S.D. 15.8	*d* 0.1	S.D. 16.5		16.5		16.4

Lat.	Twilight Naut.	Twilight Civil	Sunrise	Moonrise 12	Moonrise 13	Moonrise 14	Moonrise 15
°	h m	h m	h m	h m	h m	h m	h m
N 72	□	□	□	□	□	□	□
N 70	□	□	□	□	□	□	05 12
68	□	□	□	□	□	□	06 09
66	////	////	00 03	01 11	□	04 30	06 43
64	////	////	01 36	02 31	03 32	05 13	07 07
62	////	////	02 12	03 08	04 11	05 42	07 26
60	////	00 57	02 37	03 35	04 38	06 04	07 42
N 58	////	01 43	02 57	03 56	04 59	06 22	07 55
56	////	02 12	03 14	04 13	05 17	06 37	08 06
54	00 52	02 34	03 28	04 27	05 31	06 50	08 16
52	01 35	02 51	03 40	04 40	05 44	07 01	08 25
50	02 02	03 06	03 50	04 51	05 56	07 11	08 33
45	02 46	03 36	04 13	05 15	06 19	07 32	08 50
N 40	03 16	03 58	04 31	05 34	06 38	07 49	09 03
35	03 39	04 16	04 45	05 50	06 54	08 03	09 15
30	03 58	04 31	04 58	06 03	07 08	08 16	09 25
20	04 26	04 56	05 20	06 27	07 31	08 37	09 42
N 10	04 49	05 16	05 39	06 47	07 51	08 55	09 57
0	05 08	05 34	05 56	07 06	08 10	09 12	10 11
S 10	05 24	05 51	06 13	07 25	08 29	09 29	10 25
20	05 40	06 08	06 32	07 46	08 49	09 48	10 40
30	05 57	06 26	06 53	08 10	09 12	10 08	10 57
35	06 05	06 37	07 05	08 24	09 26	10 21	11 07
40	06 15	06 49	07 19	08 40	09 42	10 35	11 18
45	06 25	07 02	07 36	08 59	10 01	10 51	11 31
S 50	06 36	07 18	07 56	09 23	10 24	11 11	11 47
52	06 41	07 25	08 06	09 35	10 35	11 21	11 55
54	06 47	07 33	08 17	09 48	10 48	11 32	12 03
56	06 53	07 42	08 29	10 04	11 03	11 44	12 12
58	07 00	07 52	08 44	10 22	11 20	11 58	12 23
S 60	07 07	08 04	09 01	10 44	11 41	12 15	12 34

Lat.	Sunset	Twilight Civil	Twilight Naut.	Moonset 12	Moonset 13	Moonset 14	Moonset 15
°	h m	h m	h m	h m	h m	h m	h m
N 72	□	□	□	□	□	□	□
N 70	□	□	□	□	□	□	02 56
68	□	□	□	□	□	□	01 58
66	□	□	□	00 24	□	01 31	01 24
64	22 25	////	////	24 17	00 17	00 48	00 58
62	21 49	////	////	23 38	24 18	00 18	00 39
60	21 23	23 04	////	23 11	23 56	24 22	00 22
N 58	21 03	22 17	////	22 49	23 37	24 08	00 08
56	20 46	21 48	////	22 32	23 22	23 56	24 20
54	20 32	21 26	23 09	22 17	23 09	23 46	24 13
52	20 20	21 09	22 26	22 04	22 57	23 36	24 06
50	20 10	20 54	21 59	21 53	22 47	23 28	24 00
45	19 47	20 25	21 14	21 29	22 25	23 10	23 46
N 40	19 29	20 02	20 44	21 10	22 07	22 55	23 35
35	19 14	19 44	20 21	20 54	21 52	22 43	23 26
30	19 02	19 29	20 02	20 40	21 40	22 32	23 17
20	18 40	19 04	19 33	20 16	21 17	22 13	23 03
N 10	18 21	18 44	19 11	19 56	20 58	21 56	22 50
0	18 04	18 26	18 52	19 37	20 40	21 41	22 38
S 10	17 46	18 09	18 35	19 17	20 22	21 25	22 26
20	17 28	17 52	18 19	18 57	20 02	21 08	22 12
30	17 07	17 33	18 03	18 33	19 40	20 49	21 57
35	16 55	17 23	17 54	18 19	19 26	20 37	21 49
40	16 41	17 11	17 45	18 03	19 11	20 24	21 38
45	16 24	16 58	17 35	17 43	18 53	20 09	21 27
S 50	16 04	16 42	17 23	17 19	18 30	19 49	21 12
52	15 54	16 35	17 18	17 07	18 19	19 40	21 05
54	15 43	16 26	17 13	16 54	18 06	19 30	20 58
56	15 30	16 17	17 06	16 39	17 52	19 18	20 49
58	15 16	16 07	17 00	16 20	17 35	19 04	20 39
S 60	14 59	15 56	16 52	15 58	17 14	18 48	20 28

Day	SUN Eqn. of Time 00ʰ	SUN Eqn. of Time 12ʰ	SUN Mer. Pass.	MOON Mer. Pass. Upper	MOON Mer. Pass. Lower	Age	Phase
	m s	m s	h m	h m	h m	d	
12	00 26	00 20	12 00	13 21	00 50	01	
13	00 13	00 07	12 00	14 25	01 53	02	
14	00 01	00 05	12 00	15 27	02 56	03	

1983 OCTOBER 7, 8, 9 (FRI., SAT., SUN.)

	G.M.T.	ARIES	VENUS −4.2		MARS +1.9		JUPITER −1.5		SATURN +0.9		STARS		
		G.H.A.	G.H.A.	Dec.	G.H.A.	Dec.	G.H.A.	Dec.	G.H.A.	Dec.	Name	S.H.A.	Dec.
	d h	° ′	° ′	° ′	° ′	° ′	° ′	° ′	° ′	° ′		° ′	° ′
	7 00	15 04.5	223 22.9	N 8 19.0	218 22.6	N11 08.7	129 06.4	S21 07.0	162 13.3	S10 53.3	Acamar	315 35.1	S40 22.0
	01	30 06.9	238 23.7	18.8	233 23.6	08.1	144 08.4	07.1	177 15.5	53.4	Achernar	335 42.9	S57 19.1
	02	45 09.4	253 24.5	18.6	248 24.6	07.6	159 10.4	07.2	192 17.7	53.5	Acrux	173 35.7	S63 00.3
	03	60 11.8	268 25.3	· · 18.5	263 25.6	· · 07.0	174 12.4	· · 07.3	207 19.9	· · 53.6	Adhara	255 30.4	S28 56.6
	04	75 14.3	283 26.1	18.3	278 26.6	06.5	189 14.5	07.3	222 22.0	53.7	Aldebaran	291 15.3	N16 28.7
	05	90 16.8	298 27.0	18.1	293 27.6	05.9	204 16.5	07.4	237 24.2	53.8			
	06	105 19.2	313 27.8	N 8 17.9	308 28.6	N11 05.4	219 18.5	S21 07.5	252 26.4	S10 53.9	Alioth	166 41.0	N56 03.0
	07	120 21.7	328 28.6	17.7	323 29.6	04.8	234 20.5	07.6	267 28.6	54.0	Alkaid	153 17.1	N49 23.9
	08	135 24.2	343 29.4	17.5	338 30.6	04.2	249 22.5	07.6	282 30.8	54.1	Al Na'ir	28 11.7	S47 02.6
F	09	150 26.6	358 30.1	· · 17.3	353 31.6	· · 03.7	264 24.5	· · 07.7	297 33.0	· · 54.2	Alnilam	276 09.3	S 1 12.5
R	10	165 29.1	13 30.9	17.1	8 32.6	03.1	279 26.5	07.8	312 35.2	54.3	Alphard	218 18.6	S 8 35.0
I	11	180 31.6	28 31.7	16.9	23 33.6	02.6	294 28.5	07.9	327 37.4	54.4			
D	12	195 34.0	43 32.5	N 8 16.7	38 34.6	N11 02.0	309 30.5	S21 08.0	342 39.6	S10 54.5	Alphecca	126 30.5	N26 46.4
A	13	210 36.5	58 33.3	16.5	53 35.6	01.5	324 32.5	08.0	357 41.7	54.6	Alpheratz	358 06.8	N29 00.1
Y	14	225 39.0	73 34.1	16.3	68 36.6	00.9	339 34.6	08.1	12 43.9	54.7	Altair	62 30.3	N 8 49.6
	15	240 41.4	88 34.9	· · 16.1	83 37.6	11 00.4	354 36.6	· · 08.2	27 46.1	· · 54.8	Ankaa	353 37.6	S42 23.7
	16	255 43.9	103 35.7	15.9	98 38.6	10 59.8	9 38.6	08.3	42 48.3	54.9	Antares	112 54.4	S26 23.8
	17	270 46.3	118 36.4	15.7	113 39.6	59.3	24 40.6	08.3	57 50.5	55.0			
	18	285 48.8	133 37.2	N 8 15.5	128 40.6	N10 58.7	39 42.6	S21 08.4	72 52.7	S10 55.1	Arcturus	146 16.8	N19 16.2
	19	300 51.3	148 38.0	15.3	143 41.5	58.2	54 44.6	08.5	87 54.9	55.2	Atria	108 17.0	S69 00.2
	20	315 53.7	163 38.8	15.1	158 42.5	57.6	69 46.6	08.6	102 57.1	55.3	Avior	234 27.6	S59 27.0
	21	330 56.2	178 39.6	· · 14.9	173 43.5	· · 57.0	84 48.6	· · 08.6	117 59.3	· · 55.4	Bellatrix	278 56.3	N 6 20.3
	22	345 58.7	193 40.3	14.7	188 44.5	56.5	99 50.6	08.7	133 01.4	55.5	Betelgeuse	271 25.8	N 7 24.4
	23	1 01.1	208 41.1	14.5	203 45.5	55.9	114 52.6	08.8	148 03.6	55.6			
	8 00	16 03.6	223 41.9	N 8 14.3	218 46.5	N10 55.4	129 54.6	S21 08.9	163 05.8	S10 55.7	Canopus	264 06.2	S52 40.8
	01	31 06.1	238 42.6	14.1	233 47.5	54.8	144 56.6	08.9	178 08.0	55.8	Capella	281 07.9	N45 58.9
	02	46 08.5	253 43.4	13.9	248 48.5	54.3	159 58.6	09.0	193 10.2	55.9	Deneb	49 46.9	N45 13.5
	03	61 11.0	268 44.2	· · 13.7	263 49.5	· · 53.7	175 00.7	· · 09.1	208 12.4	· · 56.0	Denebola	182 57.1	N14 40.0
	04	76 13.5	283 44.9	13.5	278 50.5	53.2	190 02.7	09.2	223 14.6	56.1	Diphda	349 18.3	S18 04.5
	05	91 15.9	298 45.7	13.2	293 51.5	52.6	205 04.7	09.2	238 16.8	56.2			
	06	106 18.4	313 46.4	N 8 13.0	308 52.5	N10 52.0	220 06.7	S21 09.3	253 18.9	S10 56.3	Dubhe	194 19.8	N61 50.4
	07	121 20.8	328 47.2	12.8	323 53.5	51.5	235 08.7	09.4	268 21.1	56.4	Elnath	278 41.2	N28 35.7
S	08	136 23.3	343 47.9	12.6	338 54.5	50.9	250 10.7	09.5	283 23.3	56.5	Eltanin	90 56.9	N51 29.7
A	09	151 25.8	358 48.7	· · 12.4	353 55.5	· · 50.4	265 12.7	· · 09.5	298 25.5	· · 56.6	Enif	34 09.2	N 9 48.1
T	10	166 28.2	13 49.4	12.2	8 56.5	49.8	280 14.7	09.6	313 27.7	56.7	Fomalhaut	15 48.6	S29 42.6
U	11	181 30.7	28 50.2	11.9	23 57.5	49.3	295 16.7	09.7	328 29.9	56.8			
R	12	196 33.2	43 50.9	N 8 11.7	38 58.5	N10 48.7	310 18.7	S21 09.8	343 32.1	S10 56.9	Gacrux	172 27.1	S57 01.1
D	13	211 35.6	58 51.7	11.5	53 59.5	48.2	325 20.7	09.8	358 34.3	57.0	Gienah	176 16.1	S17 26.9
A	14	226 38.1	73 52.4	11.3	69 00.5	47.6	340 22.7	09.9	13 36.4	57.1	Hadar	149 21.0	S60 17.6
Y	15	241 40.6	88 53.2	· · 11.0	84 01.5	· · 47.0	355 24.7	· · 10.0	28 38.6	· · 57.2	Hamal	328 26.2	N23 23.2
	16	256 43.0	103 53.9	10.8	99 02.5	46.5	10 26.7	10.1	43 40.8	57.3	Kaus Aust.	84 14.0	S34 23.7
	17	271 45.5	118 54.6	10.6	114 03.5	45.9	25 28.7	10.2	58 43.0	57.4			
	18	286 47.9	133 55.4	N 8 10.4	129 04.5	N10 45.4	40 30.7	S21 10.2	73 45.2	S10 57.5	Kochab	137 19.8	N74 13.5
	19	301 50.4	148 56.1	10.1	144 05.5	44.8	55 32.7	10.3	88 47.4	57.6	Markab	14 00.7	N15 07.1
	20	316 52.9	163 56.8	09.9	159 06.5	44.3	70 34.7	10.4	103 49.6	57.7	Menkar	314 38.6	N 4 01.7
	21	331 55.3	178 57.6	· · 09.7	174 07.5	· · 43.7	85 36.7	· · 10.5	118 51.8	· · 57.8	Menkent	148 34.9	S36 17.3
	22	346 57.8	193 58.3	09.4	189 08.5	43.1	100 38.7	10.5	133 53.9	57.9	Miaplacidus	221 45.2	S69 38.6
	23	2 00.3	208 59.0	09.2	204 09.5	42.6	115 40.7	10.6	148 56.1	58.0			
	9 00	17 02.7	223 59.8	N 8 09.0	219 10.5	N10 42.0	130 42.7	S21 10.7	163 58.3	S10 58.1	Mirfak	309 12.7	N49 48.2
	01	32 05.2	239 00.5	08.7	234 11.5	41.5	145 44.7	10.8	179 00.5	58.2	Nunki	76 26.5	S26 19.2
	02	47 07.7	254 01.2	08.5	249 12.5	40.9	160 46.8	10.8	194 02.7	58.3	Peacock	53 54.6	S56 47.6
	03	62 10.1	269 01.9	· · 08.3	264 13.5	· · 40.4	175 48.8	· · 10.9	209 04.9	· · 58.4	Pollux	243 55.5	N28 04.0
	04	77 12.6	284 02.7	08.0	279 14.5	39.8	190 50.8	11.0	224 07.1	58.5	Procyon	245 23.5	N 5 16.2
	05	92 15.1	299 03.4	07.8	294 15.5	39.2	205 52.8	11.1	239 09.2	58.6			
	06	107 17.5	314 04.1	N 8 07.5	309 16.5	N10 38.7	220 54.8	S21 11.1	254 11.4	S10 58.7	Rasalhague	96 27.7	N12 34.4
	07	122 20.0	329 04.8	07.3	324 17.5	38.1	235 56.8	11.2	269 13.6	58.8	Regulus	208 07.9	N12 03.0
	08	137 22.4	344 05.5	07.1	339 18.5	37.6	250 58.8	11.3	284 15.8	58.9	Rigel	281 33.8	S 8 13.0
S	09	152 24.9	359 06.2	· · 06.8	354 19.5	· · 37.0	266 00.8	· · 11.4	299 18.0	· · 59.0	Rigil Kent.	140 23.6	S60 46.1
U	10	167 27.4	14 06.9	06.6	9 20.5	36.5	281 02.8	11.4	314 20.2	59.1	Sabik	102 38.8	S15 42.3
N	11	182 29.8	29 07.6	06.3	24 21.5	35.9	296 04.8	11.5	329 22.4	59.2			
D	12	197 32.3	44 08.3	N 8 06.1	39 22.5	N10 35.3	311 06.8	S21 11.6	344 24.6	S10 59.3	Schedar	350 06.1	N56 26.9
A	13	212 34.8	59 09.0	05.8	54 23.5	34.8	326 08.8	11.7	359 26.7	59.4	Shaula	96 53.0	S37 05.7
Y	14	227 37.2	74 09.7	05.6	69 24.5	34.2	341 10.8	11.8	14 28.9	59.5	Sirius	258 53.8	S16 41.3
	15	242 39.7	89 10.4	· · 05.3	84 25.5	· · 33.7	356 12.8	· · 11.8	29 31.1	· · 59.6	Spica	158 55.6	S11 04.4
	16	257 42.2	104 11.1	05.1	99 26.5	33.1	11 14.8	11.9	44 33.3	59.7	Suhail	223 09.5	S43 21.6
	17	272 44.6	119 11.8	04.8	114 27.5	32.5	26 16.8	12.0	59 35.5	59.8			
	18	287 47.1	134 12.5	N 8 04.6	129 28.5	N10 32.0	41 18.8	S21 12.1	74 37.7	S10 59.9	Vega	80 54.4	N38 46.3
	19	302 49.6	149 13.2	04.3	144 29.5	31.4	56 20.8	12.1	89 39.9	11 00.0	Zuben'ubi	137 30.9	S15 58.3
	20	317 52.0	164 13.9	04.1	159 30.5	30.9	71 22.8	12.2	104 42.0	00.1			
	21	332 54.5	179 14.6	· · 03.8	174 31.6	· · 30.3	86 24.8	· · 12.3	119 44.2	· · 00.2			
	22	347 56.9	194 15.3	03.5	189 32.6	29.8	101 26.8	12.4	134 46.4	00.3			
	23	2 59.4	209 16.0	03.3	204 33.6	29.2	116 28.8	12.4	149 48.6	00.4			
	Mer. Pass.	h m 22 52.0	*v* 0.7	*d* 0.2	*v* 1.0	*d* 0.6	*v* 2.0	*d* 0.1	*v* 2.2	*d* 0.1			

	S.H.A.	Mer. Pass.
	° ′	h m
Venus	207 38.3	9 05
Mars	202 42.9	9 24
Jupiter	113 51.0	15 18
Saturn	147 02.2	13 06

1983 OCTOBER 7, 8, 9 (FRI., SAT., SUN.)

	G.M.T.	SUN G.H.A.	SUN Dec.	MOON G.H.A.	MOON v	MOON Dec.	MOON d	MOON H.P.
	d h	° ′	° ′	° ′	′	° ′	′	′
	7 00	182 58.4	S 5 11.7	174 39.5	10.5	S 3 59.9	15.1	59.7
	01	197 58.6	12.6	189 09.0	10.5	4 15.0	15.0	59.7
	02	212 58.7	13.6	203 38.5	10.6	4 30.0	15.0	59.7
	03	227 58.9	·· 14.5	218 08.1	10.5	4 45.0	14.9	59.6
	04	242 59.1	15.5	232 37.6	10.6	4 59.9	14.9	59.6
	05	257 59.3	16.5	247 07.2	10.5	5 14.8	14.9	59.6
	06	272 59.5	S 5 17.4	261 36.7	10.6	S 5 29.7	14.8	59.5
	07	287 59.7	18.4	276 06.3	10.6	5 44.5	14.8	59.5
	08	302 59.8	19.3	290 35.9	10.5	5 59.3	14.7	59.5
F	09	318 00.0	·· 20.3	305 05.4	10.6	6 14.0	14.7	59.5
R	10	333 00.2	21.2	319 35.0	10.6	6 28.7	14.6	59.4
I	11	348 00.4	22.2	334 04.6	10.5	6 43.3	14.6	59.4
D	12	3 00.6	S 5 23.2	348 34.1	10.6	S 6 57.9	14.5	59.4
A	13	18 00.7	24.1	3 03.7	10.6	7 12.4	14.5	59.3
Y	14	33 00.9	25.1	17 33.3	10.6	7 26.9	14.4	59.3
	15	48 01.1	·· 26.0	32 02.9	10.5	7 41.3	14.4	59.3
	16	63 01.3	27.0	46 32.4	10.6	7 55.7	14.3	59.3
	17	78 01.5	28.0	61 02.0	10.5	8 10.0	14.3	59.2
	18	93 01.6	S 5 28.9	75 31.5	10.6	S 8 24.3	14.2	59.2
	19	108 01.8	29.9	90 01.1	10.5	8 38.5	14.1	59.2
	20	123 02.0	30.8	104 30.6	10.6	8 52.6	14.0	59.1
	21	138 02.2	·· 31.8	119 00.2	10.5	9 06.6	14.0	59.1
	22	153 02.4	32.7	133 29.7	10.6	9 20.6	14.0	59.1
	23	168 02.5	33.7	147 59.3	10.5	9 34.6	13.8	59.0
	8 00	183 02.7	S 5 34.7	162 28.8	10.5	S 9 48.4	13.8	59.0
	01	198 02.9	35.6	176 58.3	10.5	10 02.2	13.8	59.0
	02	213 03.1	36.6	191 27.8	10.5	10 16.0	13.6	58.9
	03	228 03.2	·· 37.5	205 57.3	10.5	10 29.6	13.6	58.9
	04	243 03.4	38.5	220 26.8	10.4	10 43.2	13.5	58.9
	05	258 03.6	39.4	234 56.2	10.5	10 56.7	13.4	58.8
	06	273 03.8	S 5 40.4	249 25.7	10.5	S11 10.1	13.4	58.8
	07	288 04.0	41.4	263 55.2	10.4	11 23.5	13.3	58.8
S	08	303 04.1	42.3	278 24.6	10.4	11 36.8	13.2	58.7
A	09	318 04.3	·· 43.3	292 54.0	10.4	11 50.0	13.1	58.7
T	10	333 04.5	44.2	307 23.4	10.4	12 03.1	13.1	58.7
U	11	348 04.7	45.2	321 52.8	10.4	12 16.2	12.9	58.6
R	12	3 04.8	S 5 46.1	336 22.2	10.4	S12 29.1	12.9	58.6
D	13	18 05.0	47.1	350 51.6	10.4	12 42.0	12.8	58.6
A	14	33 05.2	48.0	5 21.0	10.3	12 54.8	12.7	58.5
Y	15	48 05.4	·· 49.0	19 50.3	10.3	13 07.5	12.6	58.5
	16	63 05.5	50.0	34 19.6	10.3	13 20.1	12.6	58.5
	17	78 05.7	50.9	48 48.9	10.3	13 32.7	12.4	58.4
	18	93 05.9	S 5 51.9	63 18.2	10.3	S13 45.1	12.4	58.4
	19	108 06.1	52.8	77 47.5	10.3	13 57.5	12.3	58.4
	20	123 06.2	53.8	92 16.8	10.2	14 09.8	12.1	58.3
	21	138 06.4	·· 54.7	106 46.0	10.3	14 21.9	12.1	58.3
	22	153 06.6	55.7	121 15.3	10.2	14 34.0	12.0	58.3
	23	168 06.8	56.6	135 44.5	10.2	14 46.0	11.9	58.2
	9 00	183 06.9	S 5 57.6	150 13.7	10.1	S14 57.9	11.8	58.2
	01	198 07.1	58.5	164 42.8	10.2	15 09.7	11.7	58.2
	02	213 07.3	5 59.5	179 12.0	10.1	15 21.4	11.6	58.1
	03	228 07.5	6 00.4	193 41.1	10.2	15 33.0	11.6	58.1
	04	243 07.6	01.4	208 10.3	10.1	15 44.6	11.4	58.0
	05	258 07.8	02.4	222 39.4	10.0	15 56.0	11.3	58.0
	06	273 08.0	S 6 03.3	237 08.4	10.1	S16 07.3	11.2	58.0
	07	288 08.1	04.3	251 37.5	10.1	16 18.5	11.1	57.9
	08	303 08.3	05.2	266 06.6	10.0	16 29.6	11.0	57.9
S	09	318 08.5	·· 06.2	280 35.6	10.0	16 40.6	10.9	57.9
U	10	333 08.7	07.1	295 04.6	10.0	16 51.5	10.8	57.8
N	11	348 08.8	08.1	309 33.6	9.9	17 02.3	10.7	57.8
D	12	3 09.0	S 6 09.0	324 02.5	10.0	S17 13.0	10.6	57.8
A	13	18 09.2	10.0	338 31.5	9.9	17 23.6	10.5	57.7
Y	14	33 09.3	10.9	353 00.4	9.9	17 34.1	10.3	57.7
	15	48 09.5	·· 11.9	7 29.3	9.9	17 44.4	10.3	57.6
	16	63 09.7	12.8	21 58.2	9.9	17 54.7	10.2	57.6
	17	78 09.9	13.8	36 27.1	9.8	18 04.9	10.0	57.6
	18	93 10.0	S 6 14.7	50 55.9	9.9	S18 14.9	9.9	57.5
	19	108 10.2	15.7	65 24.8	9.8	18 24.8	9.9	57.5
	20	123 10.4	16.6	79 53.6	9.8	18 34.7	9.7	57.5
	21	138 10.5	·· 17.6	94 22.4	9.7	18 44.4	9.6	57.4
	22	153 10.7	18.5	108 51.1	9.8	18 54.0	9.4	57.4
	23	168 10.9	19.5	123 19.9	9.7	19 03.4	9.4	57.4
		S.D. 16.0	*d* 1.0	S.D. 16.2		16.0		15.7

Lat.	Twilight Naut.	Twilight Civil	Sunrise	Moonrise 7	Moonrise 8	Moonrise 9	Moonrise 10
°	h m	h m	h m	h m	h m	h m	h m
N 72	04 20	05 40	06 48	07 55	10 19	13 40	■
N 70	04 28	05 40	06 41	07 45	09 56	12 23	■
68	04 35	05 40	06 36	07 38	09 38	11 45	14 21
66	04 40	05 40	06 31	07 32	09 24	11 19	13 20
64	04 44	05 39	06 27	07 26	09 13	10 59	12 46
62	04 48	05 39	06 24	07 22	09 03	10 43	12 21
60	04 51	05 39	06 21	07 18	08 54	10 29	12 01
N 58	04 53	05 39	06 18	07 15	08 47	10 18	11 45
56	04 55	05 38	06 16	07 12	08 41	10 08	11 32
54	04 57	05 38	06 13	07 09	08 35	09 59	11 20
52	04 59	05 38	06 12	07 07	08 30	09 52	11 10
50	05 00	05 37	06 10	07 04	08 25	09 45	11 00
45	05 02	05 36	06 06	07 00	08 15	09 30	10 41
N 40	05 04	05 35	06 02	06 56	08 07	09 17	10 25
35	05 05	05 34	06 00	06 52	08 00	09 07	10 12
30	05 05	05 33	05 57	06 49	07 54	08 58	10 01
20	05 05	05 30	05 52	06 44	07 44	08 43	09 41
N 10	05 03	05 27	05 48	06 40	07 34	08 29	09 24
0	05 00	05 24	05 44	06 35	07 26	08 17	09 08
S 10	04 55	05 19	05 40	06 31	07 17	08 04	08 53
20	04 48	05 14	05 36	06 27	07 08	07 51	08 36
30	04 38	05 07	05 31	06 22	06 58	07 36	08 17
35	04 32	05 02	05 28	06 19	06 52	07 28	08 06
40	04 24	04 57	05 24	06 16	06 46	07 18	07 53
45	04 15	04 50	05 20	06 13	06 38	07 06	07 38
S 50	04 03	04 42	05 15	06 08	06 29	06 53	07 20
52	03 57	04 39	05 13	06 06	06 25	06 46	07 12
54	03 50	04 34	05 11	06 04	06 21	06 39	07 02
56	03 42	04 30	05 08	06 02	06 15	06 31	06 52
58	03 34	04 24	05 05	05 59	06 10	06 23	06 40
S 60	03 24	04 18	05 01	05 56	06 04	06 13	06 26

Lat.	Sunset	Twilight Civil	Twilight Naut.	Moonset 7	Moonset 8	Moonset 9	Moonset 10
°	h m	h m	h m	h m	h m	h m	h m
N 72	16 46	17 53	19 12	17 09	16 31	14 59	■
N 70	16 52	17 53	19 04	17 21	16 57	16 17	■
68	16 58	17 54	18 58	17 31	17 16	16 56	16 09
66	17 03	17 54	18 53	17 39	17 32	17 23	17 11
64	17 07	17 54	18 49	17 46	17 45	17 44	17 46
62	17 10	17 55	18 46	17 52	17 56	18 01	18 11
60	17 14	17 55	18 43	17 57	18 05	18 16	18 31
N 58	17 16	17 55	18 41	18 02	18 13	18 28	18 48
56	17 19	17 56	18 39	18 06	18 21	18 39	19 02
54	17 21	17 56	18 37	18 10	18 27	18 48	19 14
52	17 23	17 57	18 36	18 13	18 33	18 56	19 25
50	17 25	17 57	18 34	18 17	18 39	19 04	19 35
45	17 29	17 58	18 32	18 23	18 50	19 20	19 55
N 40	17 32	17 59	18 31	18 29	19 00	19 34	20 11
35	17 35	18 01	18 30	18 34	19 08	19 45	20 25
30	17 38	18 02	18 30	18 39	19 16	19 55	20 37
20	17 43	18 05	18 30	18 46	19 28	20 12	20 58
N 10	17 47	18 08	18 32	18 53	19 39	20 27	21 16
0	17 51	18 12	18 36	18 59	19 50	20 41	21 33
S 10	17 55	18 16	18 41	19 06	20 01	20 56	21 50
20	18 00	18 22	18 48	19 12	20 12	21 11	22 09
30	18 05	18 29	18 58	19 20	20 25	21 28	22 30
35	18 08	18 34	19 04	19 25	20 32	21 38	22 42
40	18 12	18 39	19 12	19 30	20 41	21 50	22 56
45	18 16	18 46	19 22	19 36	20 51	22 04	23 13
S 50	18 21	18 54	19 34	19 43	21 03	22 21	23 34
52	18 23	18 58	19 40	19 46	21 09	22 29	23 44
54	18 26	19 02	19 47	19 50	21 15	22 38	23 56
56	18 29	19 07	19 55	19 54	21 22	22 48	24 09
58	18 32	19 13	20 04	19 59	21 30	23 00	24 24
S 60	18 35	19 19	20 14	20 04	21 39	23 13	24 42

Day	SUN Eqn. of Time 00ʰ	SUN Eqn. of Time 12ʰ	SUN Mer. Pass.	MOON Mer. Pass. Upper	MOON Mer. Pass. Lower	MOON Age	MOON Phase
	m s	m s	h m	h m	h m	d	
7	11 53	12 02	11 48	12 47	00 22	01	
8	12 10	12 19	11 48	13 38	01 13	02	●
9	12 27	12 36	11 47	14 29	02 03	03	

16ᵐ INCREMENTS AND CORRECTIONS 17ᵐ

16ᵐ	SUN PLANETS	ARIES	MOON	v or d	Corrⁿ	v or d	Corrⁿ	v or d	Corrⁿ
s	° ′	° ′	° ′	′	′	′	′	′	′
00	4 00·0	4 00·7	3 49·1	0·0	0·0	6·0	1·7	12·0	3·3
01	4 00·3	4 00·9	3 49·3	0·1	0·0	6·1	1·7	12·1	3·3
02	4 00·5	4 01·2	3 49·5	0·2	0·1	6·2	1·7	12·2	3·4
03	4 00·8	4 01·4	3 49·8	0·3	0·1	6·3	1·7	12·3	3·4
04	4 01·0	4 01·7	3 50·0	0·4	0·1	6·4	1·8	12·4	3·4
05	4 01·3	4 01·9	3 50·3	0·5	0·1	6·5	1·8	12·5	3·4
06	4 01·5	4 02·2	3 50·5	0·6	0·2	6·6	1·8	12·6	3·5
07	4 01·8	4 02·4	3 50·7	0·7	0·2	6·7	1·8	12·7	3·5
08	4 02·0	4 02·7	3 51·0	0·8	0·2	6·8	1·9	12·8	3·5
09	4 02·3	4 02·9	3 51·2	0·9	0·2	6·9	1·9	12·9	3·5
10	4 02·5	4 03·2	3 51·5	1·0	0·3	7·0	1·9	13·0	3·6
11	4 02·8	4 03·4	3 51·7	1·1	0·3	7·1	2·0	13·1	3·6
12	4 03·0	4 03·7	3 51·9	1·2	0·3	7·2	2·0	13·2	3·6
13	4 03·3	4 03·9	3 52·2	1·3	0·4	7·3	2·0	13·3	3·7
14	4 03·5	4 04·2	3 52·4	1·4	0·4	7·4	2·0	13·4	3·7
15	4 03·8	4 04·4	3 52·6	1·5	0·4	7·5	2·1	13·5	3·7
16	4 04·0	4 04·7	3 52·9	1·6	0·4	7·6	2·1	13·6	3·7
17	4 04·3	4 04·9	3 53·1	1·7	0·5	7·7	2·1	13·7	3·8
18	4 04·5	4 05·2	3 53·4	1·8	0·5	7·8	2·1	13·8	3·8
19	4 04·8	4 05·4	3 53·6	1·9	0·5	7·9	2·2	13·9	3·8
20	4 05·0	4 05·7	3 53·8	2·0	0·6	8·0	2·2	14·0	3·9
21	4 05·3	4 05·9	3 54·1	2·1	0·6	8·1	2·2	14·1	3·9
22	4 05·5	4 06·2	3 54·3	2·2	0·6	8·2	2·3	14·2	3·9
23	4 05·8	4 06·4	3 54·6	2·3	0·6	8·3	2·3	14·3	3·9
24	4 06·0	4 06·7	3 54·8	2·4	0·7	8·4	2·3	14·4	4·0
25	4 06·3	4 06·9	3 55·0	2·5	0·7	8·5	2·3	14·5	4·0
26	4 06·5	4 07·2	3 55·3	2·6	0·7	8·6	2·4	14·6	4·0
27	4 06·8	4 07·4	3 55·5	2·7	0·7	8·7	2·4	14·7	4·0
28	4 07·0	4 07·7	3 55·7	2·8	0·8	8·8	2·4	14·8	4·1
29	4 07·3	4 07·9	3 56·0	2·9	0·8	8·9	2·4	14·9	4·1
30	4 07·5	4 08·2	3 56·2	3·0	0·8	9·0	2·5	15·0	4·1
31	4 07·8	4 08·4	3 56·5	3·1	0·9	9·1	2·5	15·1	4·2
32	4 08·0	4 08·7	3 56·7	3·2	0·9	9·2	2·5	15·2	4·2
33	4 08·3	4 08·9	3 56·9	3·3	0·9	9·3	2·6	15·3	4·2
34	4 08·5	4 09·2	3 57·2	3·4	0·9	9·4	2·6	15·4	4·2
35	4 08·8	4 09·4	3 57·4	3·5	1·0	9·5	2·6	15·5	4·3
36	4 09·0	4 09·7	3 57·7	3·6	1·0	9·6	2·6	15·6	4·3
37	4 09·3	4 09·9	3 57·9	3·7	1·0	9·7	2·7	15·7	4·3
38	4 09·5	4 10·2	3 58·1	3·8	1·0	9·8	2·7	15·8	4·3
39	4 09·8	4 10·4	3 58·4	3·9	1·1	9·9	2·7	15·9	4·4
40	4 10·0	4 10·7	3 58·6	4·0	1·1	10·0	2·8	16·0	4·4
41	4 10·3	4 10·9	3 58·8	4·1	1·1	10·1	2·8	16·1	4·4
42	4 10·5	4 11·2	3 59·1	4·2	1·2	10·2	2·8	16·2	4·5
43	4 10·8	4 11·4	3 59·3	4·3	1·2	10·3	2·8	16·3	4·5
44	4 11·0	4 11·7	3 59·6	4·4	1·2	10·4	2·9	16·4	4·5
45	4 11·3	4 11·9	3 59·8	4·5	1·2	10·5	2·9	16·5	4·5
46	4 11·5	4 12·2	4 00·0	4·6	1·3	10·6	2·9	16·6	4·6
47	4 11·8	4 12·4	4 00·3	4·7	1·3	10·7	2·9	16·7	4·6
48	4 12·0	4 12·7	4 00·5	4·8	1·3	10·8	3·0	16·8	4·6
49	4 12·3	4 12·9	4 00·8	4·9	1·3	10·9	3·0	16·9	4·6
50	4 12·5	4 13·2	4 01·0	5·0	1·4	11·0	3·0	17·0	4·7
51	4 12·8	4 13·4	4 01·2	5·1	1·4	11·1	3·1	17·1	4·7
52	4 13·0	4 13·7	4 01·5	5·2	1·4	11·2	3·1	17·2	4·7
53	4 13·3	4 13·9	4 01·7	5·3	1·5	11·3	3·1	17·3	4·8
54	4 13·5	4 14·2	4 02·0	5·4	1·5	11·4	3·1	17·4	4·8
55	4 13·8	4 14·4	4 02·2	5·5	1·5	11·5	3·2	17·5	4·8
56	4 14·0	4 14·7	4 02·4	5·6	1·5	11·6	3·2	17·6	4·8
57	4 14·3	4 14·9	4 02·7	5·7	1·6	11·7	3·2	17·7	4·9
58	4 14·5	4 15·2	4 02·9	5·8	1·6	11·8	3·2	17·8	4·9
59	4 14·8	4 15·4	4 03·1	5·9	1·6	11·9	3·3	17·9	4·9
60	4 15·0	4 15·7	4 03·4	6·0	1·7	12·0	3·3	18·0	5·0

17ᵐ	SUN PLANETS	ARIES	MOON	v or d	Corrⁿ	v or d	Corrⁿ	v or d	Corrⁿ
s	° ′	° ′	° ′	′	′	′	′	′	′
00	4 15·0	4 15·7	4 03·4	0·0	0·0	6·0	1·8	12·0	3·5
01	4 15·3	4 15·9	4 03·6	0·1	0·0	6·1	1·8	12·1	3·5
02	4 15·5	4 16·2	4 03·9	0·2	0·1	6·2	1·8	12·2	3·6
03	4 15·8	4 16·5	4 04·1	0·3	0·1	6·3	1·8	12·3	3·6
04	4 16·0	4 16·7	4 04·3	0·4	0·1	6·4	1·9	12·4	3·6
05	4 16·3	4 17·0	4 04·6	0·5	0·1	6·5	1·9	12·5	3·6
06	4 16·5	4 17·2	4 04·8	0·6	0·2	6·6	1·9	12·6	3·7
07	4 16·8	4 17·5	4 05·1	0·7	0·2	6·7	2·0	12·7	3·7
08	4 17·0	4 17·7	4 05·3	0·8	0·2	6·8	2·0	12·8	3·7
09	4 17·3	4 18·0	4 05·5	0·9	0·3	6·9	2·0	12·9	3·8
10	4 17·5	4 18·2	4 05·8	1·0	0·3	7·0	2·0	13·0	3·8
11	4 17·8	4 18·5	4 06·0	1·1	0·3	7·1	2·1	13·1	3·8
12	4 18·0	4 18·7	4 06·2	1·2	0·4	7·2	2·1	13·2	3·9
13	4 18·3	4 19·0	4 06·5	1·3	0·4	7·3	2·1	13·3	3·9
14	4 18·5	4 19·2	4 06·7	1·4	0·4	7·4	2·2	13·4	3·9
15	4 18·8	4 19·5	4 07·0	1·5	0·4	7·5	2·2	13·5	3·9
16	4 19·0	4 19·7	4 07·2	1·6	0·5	7·6	2·2	13·6	4·0
17	4 19·3	4 20·0	4 07·4	1·7	0·5	7·7	2·2	13·7	4·0
18	4 19·5	4 20·2	4 07·7	1·8	0·5	7·8	2·3	13·8	4·0
19	4 19·8	4 20·5	4 07·9	1·9	0·6	7·9	2·3	13·9	4·1
20	4 20·0	4 20·7	4 08·2	2·0	0·6	8·0	2·3	14·0	4·1
21	4 20·3	4 21·0	4 08·4	2·1	0·6	8·1	2·4	14·1	4·1
22	4 20·5	4 21·2	4 08·6	2·2	0·6	8·2	2·4	14·2	4·1
23	4 20·8	4 21·5	4 08·9	2·3	0·7	8·3	2·4	14·3	4·2
24	4 21·0	4 21·7	4 09·1	2·4	0·7	8·4	2·5	14·4	4·2
25	4 21·3	4 22·0	4 09·3	2·5	0·7	8·5	2·5	14·5	4·2
26	4 21·5	4 22·2	4 09·6	2·6	0·8	8·6	2·5	14·6	4·3
27	4 21·8	4 22·5	4 09·8	2·7	0·8	8·7	2·5	14·7	4·3
28	4 22·0	4 22·7	4 10·1	2·8	0·8	8·8	2·6	14·8	4·3
29	4 22·3	4 23·0	4 10·3	2·9	0·8	8·9	2·6	14·9	4·3
30	4 22·5	4 23·2	4 10·5	3·0	0·9	9·0	2·6	15·0	4·4
31	4 22·8	4 23·5	4 10·8	3·1	0·9	9·1	2·7	15·1	4·4
32	4 23·0	4 23·7	4 11·0	3·2	0·9	9·2	2·7	15·2	4·4
33	4 23·3	4 24·0	4 11·3	3·3	1·0	9·3	2·7	15·3	4·5
34	4 23·5	4 24·2	4 11·5	3·4	1·0	9·4	2·7	15·4	4·5
35	4 23·8	4 24·5	4 11·7	3·5	1·0	9·5	2·8	15·5	4·5
36	4 24·0	4 24·7	4 12·0	3·6	1·1	9·6	2·8	15·6	4·6
37	4 24·3	4 25·0	4 12·2	3·7	1·1	9·7	2·8	15·7	4·6
38	4 24·5	4 25·2	4 12·5	3·8	1·1	9·8	2·9	15·8	4·6
39	4 24·8	4 25·5	4 12·7	3·9	1·1	9·9	2·9	15·9	4·6
40	4 25·0	4 25·7	4 12·9	4·0	1·2	10·0	2·9	16·0	4·7
41	4 25·3	4 26·0	4 13·2	4·1	1·2	10·1	2·9	16·1	4·7
42	4 25·5	4 26·2	4 13·4	4·2	1·2	10·2	3·0	16·2	4·7
43	4 25·8	4 26·5	4 13·6	4·3	1·3	10·3	3·0	16·3	4·8
44	4 26·0	4 26·7	4 13·9	4·4	1·3	10·4	3·0	16·4	4·8
45	4 26·3	4 27·0	4 14·1	4·5	1·3	10·5	3·1	16·5	4·8
46	4 26·5	4 27·2	4 14·4	4·6	1·3	10·6	3·1	16·6	4·8
47	4 26·8	4 27·5	4 14·6	4·7	1·4	10·7	3·1	16·7	4·9
48	4 27·0	4 27·7	4 14·8	4·8	1·4	10·8	3·2	16·8	4·9
49	4 27·3	4 28·0	4 15·1	4·9	1·4	10·9	3·2	16·9	4·9
50	4 27·5	4 28·2	4 15·3	5·0	1·5	11·0	3·2	17·0	5·0
51	4 27·8	4 28·5	4 15·6	5·1	1·5	11·1	3·2	17·1	5·0
52	4 28·0	4 28·7	4 15·8	5·2	1·5	11·2	3·3	17·2	5·0
53	4 28·3	4 29·0	4 16·0	5·3	1·5	11·3	3·3	17·3	5·0
54	4 28·5	4 29·2	4 16·3	5·4	1·6	11·4	3·3	17·4	5·1
55	4 28·8	4 29·5	4 16·5	5·5	1·6	11·5	3·4	17·5	5·1
56	4 29·0	4 29·7	4 16·7	5·6	1·6	11·6	3·4	17·6	5·1
57	4 29·3	4 30·0	4 17·0	5·7	1·7	11·7	3·4	17·7	5·2
58	4 29·5	4 30·2	4 17·2	5·8	1·7	11·8	3·4	17·8	5·2
59	4 29·8	4 30·5	4 17·5	5·9	1·7	11·9	3·5	17·9	5·2
60	4 30·0	4 30·7	4 17·7	6·0	1·8	12·0	3·5	18·0	5·3

28m INCREMENTS AND CORRECTIONS 29m

28m	SUN PLANETS	ARIES	MOON	v or d	Corrⁿ	v or d	Corrⁿ	v or d	Corrⁿ
s	° ′	° ′	° ′	′	′	′	′	′	′
00	7 00·0	7 01·1	6 40·9	0·0	0·0	6·0	2·9	12·0	5·7
01	7 00·3	7 01·4	6 41·1	0·1	0·0	6·1	2·9	12·1	5·7
02	7 00·5	7 01·7	6 41·3	0·2	0·1	6·2	2·9	12·2	5·8
03	7 00·8	7 01·9	6 41·6	0·3	0·1	6·3	3·0	12·3	5·8
04	7 01·0	7 02·2	6 41·8	0·4	0·2	6·4	3·0	12·4	5·9
05	7 01·3	7 02·4	6 42·1	0·5	0·2	6·5	3·1	12·5	5·9
06	7 01·5	7 02·7	6 42·3	0·6	0·3	6·6	3·1	12·6	6·0
07	7 01·8	7 02·9	6 42·5	0·7	0·3	6·7	3·2	12·7	6·0
08	7 02·0	7 03·2	6 42·8	0·8	0·4	6·8	3·2	12·8	6·1
09	7 02·3	7 03·4	6 43·0	0·9	0·4	6·9	3·3	12·9	6·1
10	7 02·5	7 03·7	6 43·3	1·0	0·5	7·0	3·3	13·0	6·2
11	7 02·8	7 03·9	6 43·5	1·1	0·5	7·1	3·4	13·1	6·2
12	7 03·0	7 04·2	6 43·7	1·2	0·6	7·2	3·4	13·2	6·3
13	7 03·3	7 04·4	6 44·0	1·3	0·6	7·3	3·5	13·3	6·3
14	7 03·5	7 04·7	6 44·2	1·4	0·7	7·4	3·5	13·4	6·4
15	7 03·8	7 04·9	6 44·4	1·5	0·7	7·5	3·6	13·5	6·4
16	7 04·0	7 05·2	6 44·7	1·6	0·8	7·6	3·6	13·6	6·5
17	7 04·3	7 05·4	6 44·9	1·7	0·8	7·7	3·7	13·7	6·5
18	7 04·5	7 05·7	6 45·2	1·8	0·9	7·8	3·7	13·8	6·6
19	7 04·8	7 05·9	6 45·4	1·9	0·9	7·9	3·8	13·9	6·6
20	7 05·0	7 06·2	6 45·6	2·0	1·0	8·0	3·8	14·0	6·7
21	7 05·3	7 06·4	6 45·9	2·1	1·0	8·1	3·8	14·1	6·7
22	7 05·5	7 06·7	6 46·1	2·2	1·0	8·2	3·9	14·2	6·7
23	7 05·8	7 06·9	6 46·4	2·3	1·1	8·3	3·9	14·3	6·8
24	7 06·0	7 07·2	6 46·6	2·4	1·1	8·4	4·0	14·4	6·8
25	7 06·3	7 07·4	6 46·8	2·5	1·2	8·5	4·0	14·5	6·9
26	7 06·5	7 07·7	6 47·1	2·6	1·2	8·6	4·1	14·6	6·9
27	7 06·8	7 07·9	6 47·3	2·7	1·3	8·7	4·1	14·7	7·0
28	7 07·0	7 08·2	6 47·5	2·8	1·3	8·8	4·2	14·8	7·0
29	7 07·3	7 08·4	6 47·8	2·9	1·4	8·9	4·2	14·9	7·1
30	7 07·5	7 08·7	6 48·0	3·0	1·4	9·0	4·3	15·0	7·1
31	7 07·8	7 08·9	6 48·3	3·1	1·5	9·1	4·3	15·1	7·2
32	7 08·0	7 09·2	6 48·5	3·2	1·5	9·2	4·4	15·2	7·2
33	7 08·3	7 09·4	6 48·7	3·3	1·6	9·3	4·4	15·3	7·3
34	7 08·5	7 09·7	6 49·0	3·4	1·6	9·4	4·5	15·4	7·3
35	7 08·8	7 09·9	6 49·2	3·5	1·7	9·5	4·5	15·5	7·4
36	7 09·0	7 10·2	6 49·5	3·6	1·7	9·6	4·6	15·6	7·4
37	7 09·3	7 10·4	6 49·7	3·7	1·8	9·7	4·6	15·7	7·5
38	7 09·5	7 10·7	6 49·9	3·8	1·8	9·8	4·7	15·8	7·5
39	7 09·8	7 10·9	6 50·2	3·9	1·9	9·9	4·7	15·9	7·6
40	7 10·0	7 11·2	6 50·4	4·0	1·9	10·0	4·8	16·0	7·6
41	7 10·3	7 11·4	6 50·6	4·1	1·9	10·1	4·8	16·1	7·6
42	7 10·5	7 11·7	6 50·9	4·2	2·0	10·2	4·8	16·2	7·7
43	7 10·8	7 11·9	6 51·1	4·3	2·0	10·3	4·9	16·3	7·7
44	7 11·0	7 12·2	6 51·4	4·4	2·1	10·4	4·9	16·4	7·8
45	7 11·3	7 12·4	6 51·6	4·5	2·1	10·5	5·0	16·5	7·8
46	7 11·5	7 12·7	6 51·8	4·6	2·2	10·6	5·0	16·6	7·9
47	7 11·8	7 12·9	6 52·1	4·7	2·2	10·7	5·1	16·7	7·9
48	7 12·0	7 13·2	6 52·3	4·8	2·3	10·8	5·1	16·8	8·0
49	7 12·3	7 13·4	6 52·6	4·9	2·3	10·9	5·2	16·9	8·0
50	7 12·5	7 13·7	6 52·8	5·0	2·4	11·0	5·2	17·0	8·1
51	7 12·8	7 13·9	6 53·0	5·1	2·4	11·1	5·3	17·1	8·1
52	7 13·0	7 14·2	6 53·3	5·2	2·5	11·2	5·3	17·2	8·2
53	7 13·3	7 14·4	6 53·5	5·3	2·5	11·3	5·4	17·3	8·2
54	7 13·5	7 14·7	6 53·8	5·4	2·6	11·4	5·4	17·4	8·3
55	7 13·8	7 14·9	6 54·0	5·5	2·6	11·5	5·5	17·5	8·3
56	7 14·0	7 15·2	6 54·2	5·6	2·7	11·6	5·5	17·6	8·4
57	7 14·3	7 15·4	6 54·5	5·7	2·7	11·7	5·6	17·7	8·4
58	7 14·5	7 15·7	6 54·7	5·8	2·8	11·8	5·6	17·8	8·5
59	7 14·8	7 15·9	6 54·9	5·9	2·8	11·9	5·7	17·9	8·5
60	7 15·0	7 16·2	6 55·2	6·0	2·9	12·0	5·7	18·0	8·6

29m	SUN PLANETS	ARIES	MOON	v or d	Corrⁿ	v or d	Corrⁿ	v or d	Corrⁿ
s	° ′	° ′	° ′	′	′	′	′	′	′
00	7 15·0	7 16·2	6 55·2	0·0	0·0	6·0	3·0	12·0	5·9
01	7 15·3	7 16·4	6 55·4	0·1	0·0	6·1	3·0	12·1	5·9
02	7 15·5	7 16·7	6 55·7	0·2	0·1	6·2	3·0	12·2	6·0
03	7 15·8	7 16·9	6 55·9	0·3	0·1	6·3	3·1	12·3	6·0
04	7 16·0	7 17·2	6 56·1	0·4	0·2	6·4	3·1	12·4	6·1
05	7 16·3	7 17·4	6 56·4	0·5	0·2	6·5	3·2	12·5	6·1
06	7 16·5	7 17·7	6 56·6	0·6	0·3	6·6	3·2	12·6	6·2
07	7 16·8	7 17·9	6 56·9	0·7	0·3	6·7	3·3	12·7	6·2
08	7 17·0	7 18·2	6 57·1	0·8	0·4	6·8	3·3	12·8	6·3
09	7 17·3	7 18·4	6 57·3	0·9	0·4	6·9	3·4	12·9	6·3
10	7 17·5	7 18·7	6 57·6	1·0	0·5	7·0	3·4	13·0	6·4
11	7 17·8	7 18·9	6 57·8	1·1	0·5	7·1	3·5	13·1	6·4
12	7 18·0	7 19·2	6 58·0	1·2	0·6	7·2	3·5	13·2	6·5
13	7 18·3	7 19·4	6 58·3	1·3	0·6	7·3	3·6	13·3	6·5
14	7 18·5	7 19·7	6 58·5	1·4	0·7	7·4	3·6	13·4	6·6
15	7 18·8	7 20·0	6 58·8	1·5	0·7	7·5	3·7	13·5	6·6
16	7 19·0	7 20·2	6 59·0	1·6	0·8	7·6	3·7	13·6	6·7
17	7 19·3	7 20·5	6 59·2	1·7	0·8	7·7	3·8	13·7	6·7
18	7 19·5	7 20·7	6 59·5	1·8	0·9	7·8	3·8	13·8	6·8
19	7 19·8	7 21·0	6 59·7	1·9	0·9	7·9	3·9	13·9	6·8
20	7 20·0	7 21·2	7 00·0	2·0	1·0	8·0	3·9	14·0	6·9
21	7 20·3	7 21·5	7 00·2	2·1	1·0	8·1	4·0	14·1	6·9
22	7 20·5	7 21·7	7 00·4	2·2	1·1	8·2	4·0	14·2	7·0
23	7 20·8	7 22·0	7 00·7	2·3	1·1	8·3	4·1	14·3	7·0
24	7 21·0	7 22·2	7 00·9	2·4	1·2	8·4	4·1	14·4	7·1
25	7 21·3	7 22·5	7 01·1	2·5	1·2	8·5	4·2	14·5	7·1
26	7 21·5	7 22·7	7 01·4	2·6	1·3	8·6	4·2	14·6	7·2
27	7 21·8	7 23·0	7 01·6	2·7	1·3	8·7	4·3	14·7	7·2
28	7 22·0	7 23·2	7 01·9	2·8	1·4	8·8	4·3	14·8	7·3
29	7 22·3	7 23·5	7 02·1	2·9	1·4	8·9	4·4	14·9	7·3
30	7 22·5	7 23·7	7 02·3	3·0	1·5	9·0	4·4	15·0	7·4
31	7 22·8	7 24·0	7 02·6	3·1	1·5	9·1	4·5	15·1	7·4
32	7 23·0	7 24·2	7 02·8	3·2	1·6	9·2	4·5	15·2	7·5
33	7 23·3	7 24·5	7 03·1	3·3	1·6	9·3	4·6	15·3	7·5
34	7 23·5	7 24·7	7 03·3	3·4	1·7	9·4	4·6	15·4	7·6
35	7 23·8	7 25·0	7 03·5	3·5	1·7	9·5	4·7	15·5	7·6
36	7 24·0	7 25·2	7 03·8	3·6	1·8	9·6	4·7	15·6	7·7
37	7 24·3	7 25·5	7 04·0	3·7	1·8	9·7	4·8	15·7	7·7
38	7 24·5	7 25·7	7 04·3	3·8	1·9	9·8	4·8	15·8	7·8
39	7 24·8	7 26·0	7 04·5	3·9	1·9	9·9	4·9	15·9	7·8
40	7 25·0	7 26·2	7 04·7	4·0	2·0	10·0	4·9	16·0	7·9
41	7 25·3	7 26·5	7 05·0	4·1	2·0	10·1	5·0	16·1	7·9
42	7 25·5	7 26·7	7 05·2	4·2	2·1	10·2	5·0	16·2	8·0
43	7 25·8	7 27·0	7 05·4	4·3	2·1	10·3	5·1	16·3	8·0
44	7 26·0	7 27·2	7 05·7	4·4	2·2	10·4	5·1	16·4	8·1
45	7 26·3	7 27·5	7 05·9	4·5	2·2	10·5	5·2	16·5	8·1
46	7 26·5	7 27·7	7 06·2	4·6	2·3	10·6	5·2	16·6	8·2
47	7 26·8	7 28·0	7 06·4	4·7	2·3	10·7	5·3	16·7	8·2
48	7 27·0	7 28·2	7 06·6	4·8	2·4	10·8	5·3	16·8	8·3
49	7 27·3	7 28·5	7 06·9	4·9	2·4	10·9	5·4	16·9	8·3
50	7 27·5	7 28·7	7 07·1	5·0	2·5	11·0	5·4	17·0	8·4
51	7 27·8	7 29·0	7 07·4	5·1	2·5	11·1	5·5	17·1	8·4
52	7 28·0	7 29·2	7 07·6	5·2	2·6	11·2	5·5	17·2	8·5
53	7 28·3	7 29·5	7 07·8	5·3	2·6	11·3	5·6	17·3	8·5
54	7 28·5	7 29·7	7 08·1	5·4	2·7	11·4	5·6	17·4	8·6
55	7 28·8	7 30·0	7 08·3	5·5	2·7	11·5	5·7	17·5	8·6
56	7 29·0	7 30·2	7 08·5	5·6	2·8	11·6	5·7	17·6	8·7
57	7 29·3	7 30·5	7 08·8	5·7	2·8	11·7	5·8	17·7	8·7
58	7 29·5	7 30·7	7 09·0	5·8	2·9	11·8	5·8	17·8	8·8
59	7 29·8	7 31·0	7 09·3	5·9	2·9	11·9	5·9	17·9	8·8
60	7 30·0	7 31·2	7 09·5	6·0	3·0	12·0	5·9	18·0	8·9

40^m INCREMENTS AND CORRECTIONS 41^m

40^m	SUN PLANETS	ARIES	MOON	v or d	Corr^n	v or d	Corr^n	v or d	Corr^n
s	° ′	° ′	° ′	′	′	′	′	′	′
00	10 00·0	10 01·6	9 32·7	0·0	0·0	6·0	4·1	12·0	8·1
01	10 00·3	10 01·9	9 32·9	0·1	0·1	6·1	4·1	12·1	8·2
02	10 00·5	10 02·1	9 33·1	0·2	0·1	6·2	4·2	12·2	8·2
03	10 00·8	10 02·4	9 33·4	0·3	0·2	6·3	4·3	12·3	8·3
04	10 01·0	10 02·6	9 33·6	0·4	0·3	6·4	4·3	12·4	8·4
05	10 01·3	10 02·9	9 33·9	0·5	0·3	6·5	4·4	12·5	8·4
06	10 01·5	10 03·1	9 34·1	0·6	0·4	6·6	4·5	12·6	8·5
07	10 01·8	10 03·4	9 34·3	0·7	0·5	6·7	4·5	12·7	8·6
08	10 02·0	10 03·6	9 34·6	0·8	0·5	6·8	4·6	12·8	8·6
09	10 02·3	10 03·9	9 34·8	0·9	0·6	6·9	4·7	12·9	8·7
10	10 02·5	10 04·1	9 35·1	1·0	0·7	7·0	4·7	13·0	8·8
11	10 02·8	10 04·4	9 35·3	1·1	0·7	7·1	4·8	13·1	8·8
12	10 03·0	10 04·7	9 35·5	1·2	0·8	7·2	4·9	13·2	8·9
13	10 03·3	10 04·9	9 35·8	1·3	0·9	7·3	4·9	13·3	9·0
14	10 03·5	10 05·2	9 36·0	1·4	0·9	7·4	5·0	13·4	9·0
15	10 03·8	10 05·4	9 36·2	1·5	1·0	7·5	5·1	13·5	9·1
16	10 04·0	10 05·7	9 36·5	1·6	1·1	7·6	5·1	13·6	9·2
17	10 04·3	10 05·9	9 36·7	1·7	1·1	7·7	5·2	13·7	9·2
18	10 04·5	10 06·2	9 37·0	1·8	1·2	7·8	5·3	13·8	9·3
19	10 04·8	10 06·4	9 37·2	1·9	1·3	7·9	5·3	13·9	9·4
20	10 05·0	10 06·7	9 37·4	2·0	1·4	8·0	5·4	14·0	9·5
21	10 05·3	10 06·9	9 37·7	2·1	1·4	8·1	5·5	14·1	9·5
22	10 05·5	10 07·2	9 37·9	2·2	1·5	8·2	5·5	14·2	9·6
23	10 05·8	10 07·4	9 38·2	2·3	1·6	8·3	5·6	14·3	9·7
24	10 06·0	10 07·7	9 38·4	2·4	1·6	8·4	5·7	14·4	9·7
25	10 06·3	10 07·9	9 38·6	2·5	1·7	8·5	5·7	14·5	9·8
26	10 06·5	10 08·2	9 38·9	2·6	1·8	8·6	5·8	14·6	9·9
27	10 06·8	10 08·4	9 39·1	2·7	1·8	8·7	5·9	14·7	9·9
28	10 07·0	10 08·7	9 39·3	2·8	1·9	8·8	5·9	14·8	10·0
29	10 07·3	10 08·9	9 39·6	2·9	2·0	8·9	6·0	14·9	10·1
30	10 07·5	10 09·2	9 39·8	3·0	2·0	9·0	6·1	15·0	10·1
31	10 07·8	10 09·4	9 40·1	3·1	2·1	9·1	6·1	15·1	10·2
32	10 08·0	10 09·7	9 40·3	3·2	2·2	9·2	6·2	15·2	10·3
33	10 08·3	10 09·9	9 40·5	3·3	2·2	9·3	6·3	15·3	10·3
34	10 08·5	10 10·2	9 40·8	3·4	2·3	9·4	6·3	15·4	10·4
35	10 08·8	10 10·4	9 41·0	3·5	2·4	9·5	6·4	15·5	10·5
36	10 09·0	10 10·7	9 41·3	3·6	2·4	9·6	6·5	15·6	10·5
37	10 09·3	10 10·9	9 41·5	3·7	2·5	9·7	6·5	15·7	10·6
38	10 09·5	10 11·2	9 41·7	3·8	2·6	9·8	6·6	15·8	10·7
39	10 09·8	10 11·4	9 42·0	3·9	2·6	9·9	6·7	15·9	10·7
40	10 10·0	10 11·7	9 42·2	4·0	2·7	10·0	6·8	16·0	10·8
41	10 10·3	10 11·9	9 42·4	4·1	2·8	10·1	6·8	16·1	10·9
42	10 10·5	10 12·2	9 42·7	4·2	2·8	10·2	6·9	16·2	10·9
43	10 10·8	10 12·4	9 42·9	4·3	2·9	10·3	7·0	16·3	11·0
44	10 11·0	10 12·7	9 43·2	4·4	3·0	10·4	7·0	16·4	11·1
45	10 11·3	10 12·9	9 43·4	4·5	3·0	10·5	7·1	16·5	11·1
46	10 11·5	10 13·2	9 43·6	4·6	3·1	10·6	7·2	16·6	11·2
47	10 11·8	10 13·4	9 43·9	4·7	3·2	10·7	7·2	16·7	11·3
48	10 12·0	10 13·7	9 44·1	4·8	3·2	10·8	7·3	16·8	11·3
49	10 12·3	10 13·9	9 44·4	4·9	3·3	10·9	7·4	16·9	11·4
50	10 12·5	10 14·2	9 44·6	5·0	3·4	11·0	7·4	17·0	11·5
51	10 12·8	10 14·4	9 44·8	5·1	3·4	11·1	7·5	17·1	11·5
52	10 13·0	10 14·7	9 45·1	5·2	3·5	11·2	7·6	17·2	11·6
53	10 13·3	10 14·9	9 45·3	5·3	3·6	11·3	7·6	17·3	11·7
54	10 13·5	10 15·2	9 45·6	5·4	3·6	11·4	7·7	17·4	11·7
55	10 13·8	10 15·4	9 45·8	5·5	3·7	11·5	7·8	17·5	11·8
56	10 14·0	10 15·7	9 46·0	5·6	3·8	11·6	7·8	17·6	11·9
57	10 14·3	10 15·9	9 46·3	5·7	3·8	11·7	7·9	17·7	11·9
58	10 14·5	10 16·2	9 46·5	5·8	3·9	11·8	8·0	17·8	12·0
59	10 14·8	10 16·4	9 46·7	5·9	4·0	11·9	8·0	17·9	12·1
60	10 15·0	10 16·7	9 47·0	6·0	4·1	12·0	8·1	18·0	12·2

41^m	SUN PLANETS	ARIES	MOON	v or d	Corr^n	v or d	Corr^n	v or d	Corr^n
s	° ′	° ′	° ′	′	′	′	′	′	′
00	10 15·0	10 16·7	9 47·0	0·0	0·0	6·0	4·2	12·0	8·3
01	10 15·3	10 16·9	9 47·2	0·1	0·1	6·1	4·2	12·1	8·4
02	10 15·5	10 17·2	9 47·5	0·2	0·1	6·2	4·3	12·2	8·4
03	10 15·8	10 17·4	9 47·7	0·3	0·2	6·3	4·4	12·3	8·5
04	10 16·0	10 17·7	9 47·9	0·4	0·3	6·4	4·4	12·4	8·6
05	10 16·3	10 17·9	9 48·2	0·5	0·3	6·5	4·5	12·5	8·6
06	10 16·5	10 18·2	9 48·4	0·6	0·4	6·6	4·6	12·6	8·7
07	10 16·8	10 18·4	9 48·7	0·7	0·5	6·7	4·6	12·7	8·8
08	10 17·0	10 18·7	9 48·9	0·8	0·6	6·8	4·7	12·8	8·9
09	10 17·3	10 18·9	9 49·1	0·9	0·6	6·9	4·8	12·9	8·9
10	10 17·5	10 19·2	9 49·4	1·0	0·7	7·0	4·8	13·0	9·0
11	10 17·8	10 19·4	9 49·6	1·1	0·8	7·1	4·9	13·1	9·1
12	10 18·0	10 19·7	9 49·8	1·2	0·8	7·2	5·0	13·2	9·1
13	10 18·3	10 19·9	9 50·1	1·3	0·9	7·3	5·0	13·3	9·2
14	10 18·5	10 20·2	9 50·3	1·4	1·0	7·4	5·1	13·4	9·3
15	10 18·8	10 20·4	9 50·6	1·5	1·0	7·5	5·2	13·5	9·3
16	10 19·0	10 20·7	9 50·8	1·6	1·1	7·6	5·3	13·6	9·4
17	10 19·3	10 20·9	9 51·0	1·7	1·2	7·7	5·3	13·7	9·5
18	10 19·5	10 21·2	9 51·3	1·8	1·2	7·8	5·4	13·8	9·5
19	10 19·8	10 21·4	9 51·5	1·9	1·3	7·9	5·5	13·9	9·6
20	10 20·0	10 21·7	9 51·8	2·0	1·4	8·0	5·5	14·0	9·7
21	10 20·3	10 21·9	9 52·0	2·1	1·5	8·1	5·6	14·1	9·8
22	10 20·5	10 22·2	9 52·2	2·2	1·5	8·2	5·7	14·2	9·8
23	10 20·8	10 22·4	9 52·5	2·3	1·6	8·3	5·7	14·3	9·9
24	10 21·0	10 22·7	9 52·7	2·4	1·7	8·4	5·8	14·4	10·0
25	10 21·3	10 23·0	9 52·9	2·5	1·7	8·5	5·9	14·5	10·0
26	10 21·5	10 23·2	9 53·2	2·6	1·8	8·6	5·9	14·6	10·1
27	10 21·8	10 23·5	9 53·4	2·7	1·9	8·7	6·0	14·7	10·2
28	10 22·0	10 23·7	9 53·7	2·8	1·9	8·8	6·1	14·8	10·2
29	10 22·3	10 24·0	9 53·9	2·9	2·0	8·9	6·2	14·9	10·3
30	10 22·5	10 24·2	9 54·1	3·0	2·1	9·0	6·2	15·0	10·4
31	10 22·8	10 24·5	9 54·4	3·1	2·1	9·1	6·3	15·1	10·4
32	10 23·0	10 24·7	9 54·6	3·2	2·2	9·2	6·4	15·2	10·5
33	10 23·3	10 25·0	9 54·9	3·3	2·3	9·3	6·4	15·3	10·6
34	10 23·5	10 25·2	9 55·1	3·4	2·4	9·4	6·5	15·4	10·7
35	10 23·8	10 25·5	9 55·3	3·5	2·4	9·5	6·6	15·5	10·7
36	10 24·0	10 25·7	9 55·6	3·6	2·5	9·6	6·6	15·6	10·8
37	10 24·3	10 26·0	9 55·8	3·7	2·6	9·7	6·7	15·7	10·9
38	10 24·5	10 26·2	9 56·1	3·8	2·6	9·8	6·8	15·8	10·9
39	10 24·8	10 26·5	9 56·3	3·9	2·7	9·9	6·8	15·9	11·0
40	10 25·0	10 26·7	9 56·5	4·0	2·8	10·0	6·9	16·0	11·1
41	10 25·3	10 27·0	9 56·8	4·1	2·8	10·1	7·0	16·1	11·1
42	10 25·5	10 27·2	9 57·0	4·2	2·9	10·2	7·1	16·2	11·2
43	10 25·8	10 27·5	9 57·2	4·3	3·0	10·3	7·1	16·3	11·3
44	10 26·0	10 27·7	9 57·5	4·4	3·0	10·4	7·2	16·4	11·3
45	10 26·3	10 28·0	9 57·7	4·5	3·1	10·5	7·3	16·5	11·4
46	10 26·5	10 28·2	9 58·0	4·6	3·2	10·6	7·3	16·6	11·5
47	10 26·8	10 28·5	9 58·2	4·7	3·3	10·7	7·4	16·7	11·6
48	10 27·0	10 28·7	9 58·4	4·8	3·3	10·8	7·5	16·8	11·6
49	10 27·3	10 29·0	9 58·7	4·9	3·4	10·9	7·5	16·9	11·7
50	10 27·5	10 29·2	9 58·9	5·0	3·5	11·0	7·6	17·0	11·8
51	10 27·8	10 29·5	9 59·2	5·1	3·5	11·1	7·7	17·1	11·8
52	10 28·0	10 29·7	9 59·4	5·2	3·6	11·2	7·7	17·2	11·9
53	10 28·3	10 30·0	9 59·6	5·3	3·7	11·3	7·8	17·3	12·0
54	10 28·5	10 30·2	9 59·9	5·4	3·7	11·4	7·9	17·4	12·0
55	10 28·8	10 30·5	10 00·1	5·5	3·8	11·5	8·0	17·5	12·1
56	10 29·0	10 30·7	10 00·3	5·6	3·9	11·6	8·0	17·6	12·2
57	10 29·3	10 31·0	10 00·6	5·7	3·9	11·7	8·1	17·7	12·2
58	10 29·5	10 31·2	10 00·8	5·8	4·0	11·8	8·2	17·8	12·3
59	10 29·8	10 31·5	10 01·1	5·9	4·1	11·9	8·2	17·9	12·4
60	10 30·0	10 31·7	10 01·3	6·0	4·2	12·0	8·3	18·0	12·5

54ᵐ INCREMENTS AND CORRECTIONS 55ᵐ

54ᵐ s	SUN PLANETS ° ′	ARIES ° ′	MOON ° ′	v or d ′	Corrⁿ ′	v or d ′	Corrⁿ ′	v or d ′	Corrⁿ ′
00	13 30·0	13 32·2	12 53·1	0·0	0·0	6·0	5·5	12·0	10·9
01	13 30·3	13 32·5	12 53·3	0·1	0·1	6·1	5·5	12·1	11·0
02	13 30·5	13 32·7	12 53·6	0·2	0·2	6·2	5·6	12·2	11·1
03	13 30·8	13 33·0	12 53·8	0·3	0·3	6·3	5·7	12·3	11·2
04	13 31·0	13 33·2	12 54·1	0·4	0·4	6·4	5·8	12·4	11·3
05	13 31·3	13 33·5	12 54·3	0·5	0·5	6·5	5·9	12·5	11·4
06	13 31·5	13 33·7	12 54·5	0·6	0·5	6·6	6·0	12·6	11·4
07	13 31·8	13 34·0	12 54·8	0·7	0·6	6·7	6·1	12·7	11·5
08	13 32·0	13 34·2	12 55·0	0·8	0·7	6·8	6·2	12·8	11·6
09	13 32·3	13 34·5	12 55·2	0·9	0·8	6·9	6·3	12·9	11·7
10	13 32·5	13 34·7	12 55·5	1·0	0·9	7·0	6·4	13·0	11·8
11	13 32·8	13 35·0	12 55·7	1·1	1·0	7·1	6·4	13·1	11·9
12	13 33·0	13 35·2	12 56·0	1·2	1·1	7·2	6·5	13·2	12·0
13	13 33·3	13 35·5	12 56·2	1·3	1·2	7·3	6·6	13·3	12·1
14	13 33·5	13 35·7	12 56·4	1·4	1·3	7·4	6·7	13·4	12·2
15	13 33·8	13 36·0	12 56·7	1·5	1·4	7·5	6·8	13·5	12·3
16	13 34·0	13 36·2	12 56·9	1·6	1·5	7·6	6·9	13·6	12·4
17	13 34·3	13 36·5	12 57·2	1·7	1·5	7·7	7·0	13·7	12·4
18	13 34·5	13 36·7	12 57·4	1·8	1·6	7·8	7·1	13·8	12·5
19	13 34·8	13 37·0	12 57·6	1·9	1·7	7·9	7·2	13·9	12·6
20	13 35·0	13 37·2	12 57·9	2·0	1·8	8·0	7·3	14·0	12·7
21	13 35·3	13 37·5	12 58·1	2·1	1·9	8·1	7·4	14·1	12·8
22	13 35·5	13 37·7	12 58·3	2·2	2·0	8·2	7·4	14·2	12·9
23	13 35·8	13 38·0	12 58·6	2·3	2·1	8·3	7·5	14·3	13·0
24	13 36·0	13 38·2	12 58·8	2·4	2·2	8·4	7·6	14·4	13·1
25	13 36·3	13 38·5	12 59·1	2·5	2·3	8·5	7·7	14·5	13·2
26	13 36·5	13 38·7	12 59·3	2·6	2·4	8·6	7·8	14·6	13·3
27	13 36·8	13 39·0	12 59·5	2·7	2·5	8·7	7·9	14·7	13·4
28	13 37·0	13 39·2	12 59·8	2·8	2·5	8·8	8·0	14·8	13·4
29	13 37·3	13 39·5	13 00·0	2·9	2·6	8·9	8·1	14·9	13·5
30	13 37·5	13 39·7	13 00·3	3·0	2·7	9·0	8·2	15·0	13·6
31	13 37·8	13 40·0	13 00·5	3·1	2·8	9·1	8·3	15·1	13·7
32	13 38·0	13 40·2	13 00·7	3·2	2·9	9·2	8·4	15·2	13·8
33	13 38·3	13 40·5	13 01·0	3·3	3·0	9·3	8·4	15·3	13·9
34	13 38·5	13 40·7	13 01·2	3·4	3·1	9·4	8·5	15·4	14·0
35	13 38·8	13 41·0	13 01·5	3·5	3·2	9·5	8·6	15·5	14·1
36	13 39·0	13 41·2	13 01·7	3·6	3·3	9·6	8·7	15·6	14·2
37	13 39·3	13 41·5	13 01·9	3·7	3·4	9·7	8·8	15·7	14·3
38	13 39·5	13 41·7	13 02·2	3·8	3·5	9·8	8·9	15·8	14·4
39	13 39·8	13 42·0	13 02·4	3·9	3·5	9·9	9·0	15·9	14·4
40	13 40·0	13 42·2	13 02·6	4·0	3·6	10·0	9·1	16·0	14·5
41	13 40·3	13 42·5	13 02·9	4·1	3·7	10·1	9·2	16·1	14·6
42	13 40·5	13 42·7	13 03·1	4·2	3·8	10·2	9·3	16·2	14·7
43	13 40·8	13 43·0	13 03·4	4·3	3·9	10·3	9·4	16·3	14·8
44	13 41·0	13 43·2	13 03·6	4·4	4·0	10·4	9·4	16·4	14·9
45	13 41·3	13 43·5	13 03·8	4·5	4·1	10·5	9·5	16·5	15·0
46	13 41·5	13 43·7	13 04·1	4·6	4·2	10·6	9·6	16·6	15·1
47	13 41·8	13 44·0	13 04·3	4·7	4·3	10·7	9·7	16·7	15·2
48	13 42·0	13 44·3	13 04·6	4·8	4·4	10·8	9·8	16·8	15·3
49	13 42·3	13 44·5	13 04·8	4·9	4·5	10·9	9·9	16·9	15·4
50	13 42·5	13 44·8	13 05·0	5·0	4·5	11·0	10·0	17·0	15·4
51	13 42·8	13 45·0	13 05·3	5·1	4·6	11·1	10·1	17·1	15·5
52	13 43·0	13 45·3	13 05·5	5·2	4·7	11·2	10·2	17·2	15·6
53	13 43·3	13 45·5	13 05·7	5·3	4·8	11·3	10·3	17·3	15·7
54	13 43·5	13 45·8	13 06·0	5·4	4·9	11·4	10·4	17·4	15·8
55	13 43·8	13 46·0	13 06·2	5·5	5·0	11·5	10·4	17·5	15·9
56	13 44·0	13 46·3	13 06·5	5·6	5·1	11·6	10·5	17·6	16·0
57	13 44·3	13 46·5	13 06·7	5·7	5·2	11·7	10·6	17·7	16·1
58	13 44·5	13 46·8	13 06·9	5·8	5·3	11·8	10·7	17·8	16·2
59	13 44·8	13 47·0	13 07·2	5·9	5·4	11·9	10·8	17·9	16·3
60	13 45·0	13 47·3	13 07·4	6·0	5·5	12·0	10·9	18·0	16·4

55ᵐ s	SUN PLANETS ° ′	ARIES ° ′	MOON ° ′	v or d ′	Corrⁿ ′	v or d ′	Corrⁿ ′	v or d ′	Corrⁿ ′
00	13 45·0	13 47·3	13 07·4	0·0	0·0	6·0	5·6	12·0	11·1
01	13 45·3	13 47·5	13 07·7	0·1	0·1	6·1	5·6	12·1	11·2
02	13 45·5	13 47·8	13 07·9	0·2	0·2	6·2	5·7	12·2	11·3
03	13 45·8	13 48·0	13 08·1	0·3	0·3	6·3	5·8	12·3	11·4
04	13 46·0	13 48·3	13 08·4	0·4	0·4	6·4	5·9	12·4	11·5
05	13 46·3	13 48·5	13 08·6	0·5	0·5	6·5	6·0	12·5	11·6
06	13 46·5	13 48·8	13 08·8	0·6	0·6	6·6	6·1	12·6	11·7
07	13 46·8	13 49·0	13 09·1	0·7	0·6	6·7	6·2	12·7	11·7
08	13 47·0	13 49·3	13 09·3	0·8	0·7	6·8	6·3	12·8	11·8
09	13 47·3	13 49·5	13 09·6	0·9	0·8	6·9	6·4	12·9	11·9
10	13 47·5	13 49·8	13 09·8	1·0	0·9	7·0	6·5	13·0	12·0
11	13 47·8	13 50·0	13 10·0	1·1	1·0	7·1	6·6	13·1	12·1
12	13 48·0	13 50·3	13 10·3	1·2	1·1	7·2	6·7	13·2	12·2
13	13 48·3	13 50·5	13 10·5	1·3	1·2	7·3	6·8	13·3	12·3
14	13 48·5	13 50·8	13 10·8	1·4	1·3	7·4	6·8	13·4	12·4
15	13 48·8	13 51·0	13 11·0	1·5	1·4	7·5	6·9	13·5	12·5
16	13 49·0	13 51·3	13 11·2	1·6	1·5	7·6	7·0	13·6	12·6
17	13 49·3	13 51·5	13 11·5	1·7	1·6	7·7	7·1	13·7	12·7
18	13 49·5	13 51·8	13 11·7	1·8	1·7	7·8	7·2	13·8	12·8
19	13 49·8	13 52·0	13 12·0	1·9	1·8	7·9	7·3	13·9	12·9
20	13 50·0	13 52·3	13 12·2	2·0	1·9	8·0	7·4	14·0	13·0
21	13 50·3	13 52·5	13 12·4	2·1	1·9	8·1	7·5	14·1	13·0
22	13 50·5	13 52·8	13 12·7	2·2	2·0	8·2	7·6	14·2	13·1
23	13 50·8	13 53·0	13 12·9	2·3	2·1	8·3	7·7	14·3	13·2
24	13 51·0	13 53·3	13 13·1	2·4	2·2	8·4	7·8	14·4	13·3
25	13 51·3	13 53·5	13 13·4	2·5	2·3	8·5	7·9	14·5	13·4
26	13 51·5	13 53·8	13 13·6	2·6	2·4	8·6	8·0	14·6	13·5
27	13 51·8	13 54·0	13 13·9	2·7	2·5	8·7	8·0	14·7	13·6
28	13 52·0	13 54·3	13 14·1	2·8	2·6	8·8	8·1	14·8	13·7
29	13 52·3	13 54·5	13 14·3	2·9	2·7	8·9	8·2	14·9	13·8
30	13 52·5	13 54·8	13 14·6	3·0	2·8	9·0	8·3	15·0	13·9
31	13 52·8	13 55·0	13 14·8	3·1	2·9	9·1	8·4	15·1	14·0
32	13 53·0	13 55·3	13 15·1	3·2	3·0	9·2	8·5	15·2	14·1
33	13 53·3	13 55·5	13 15·3	3·3	3·1	9·3	8·6	15·3	14·2
34	13 53·5	13 55·8	13 15·5	3·4	3·1	9·4	8·7	15·4	14·2
35	13 53·8	13 56·0	13 15·8	3·5	3·2	9·5	8·8	15·5	14·3
36	13 54·0	13 56·3	13 16·0	3·6	3·3	9·6	8·9	15·6	14·4
37	13 54·3	13 56·5	13 16·2	3·7	3·4	9·7	9·0	15·7	14·5
38	13 54·5	13 56·8	13 16·5	3·8	3·5	9·8	9·1	15·8	14·6
39	13 54·8	13 57·0	13 16·7	3·9	3·6	9·9	9·2	15·9	14·7
40	13 55·0	13 57·3	13 17·0	4·0	3·7	10·0	9·3	16·0	14·8
41	13 55·3	13 57·5	13 17·2	4·1	3·8	10·1	9·3	16·1	14·9
42	13 55·5	13 57·8	13 17·4	4·2	3·9	10·2	9·4	16·2	15·0
43	13 55·8	13 58·0	13 17·7	4·3	4·0	10·3	9·5	16·3	15·1
44	13 56·0	13 58·3	13 17·9	4·4	4·1	10·4	9·6	16·4	15·2
45	13 56·3	13 58·5	13 18·2	4·5	4·2	10·5	9·7	16·5	15·3
46	13 56·5	13 58·8	13 18·4	4·6	4·3	10·6	9·8	16·6	15·4
47	13 56·8	13 59·0	13 18·6	4·7	4·3	10·7	9·9	16·7	15·4
48	13 57·0	13 59·3	13 18·9	4·8	4·4	10·8	10·0	16·8	15·5
49	13 57·3	13 59·5	13 19·1	4·9	4·5	10·9	10·1	16·9	15·6
50	13 57·5	13 59·8	13 19·3	5·0	4·6	11·0	10·2	17·0	15·7
51	13 57·8	14 00·0	13 19·6	5·1	4·7	11·1	10·3	17·1	15·8
52	13 58·0	14 00·3	13 19·8	5·2	4·8	11·2	10·4	17·2	15·9
53	13 58·3	14 00·5	13 20·1	5·3	4·9	11·3	10·5	17·3	16·0
54	13 58·5	14 00·8	13 20·3	5·4	5·0	11·4	10·5	17·4	16·1
55	13 58·8	14 01·0	13 20·5	5·5	5·1	11·5	10·6	17·5	16·2
56	13 59·0	14 01·3	13 20·8	5·6	5·2	11·6	10·7	17·6	16·3
57	13 59·3	14 01·5	13 21·0	5·7	5·3	11·7	10·8	17·7	16·4
58	13 59·5	14 01·8	13 21·3	5·8	5·4	11·8	10·9	17·8	16·5
59	13 59·8	14 02·0	13 21·5	5·9	5·5	11·9	11·0	17·9	16·6
60	14 00·0	14 02·3	13 21·7	6·0	5·6	12·0	11·1	18·0	16·7

LAT 46°S

LHA ♈	Hc Zn	Hc Zn	Hc Zn	Hc Zn	Hc Zn	Hc Zn	Hc Zn
	BETELGEUSE	SIRIUS	♦Suhail	RIGIL KENT.	♦ACHERNAR	Diphda	♦ALDEBARAN
85	36 30 004	57 46 030	53 41 105	22 55 158	52 05 230	23 42 268	25 49 343
86	36 33 003	58 06 028	54 22 105	23 11 157	51 33 230	23 00 267	25 36 342
87	36 35 002	58 25 027	55 02 104	23 27 157	51 01 230	22 19 267	25 23 341
88	36 36 001	58 43 025	55 43 104	23 44 157	50 30 230	21 37 266	25 09 340
89	36 36 359	59 00 023	56 23 103	24 00 156	49 58 229	20 55 265	24 54 339

LAT 46°N

LHA ♈	Hc Zn	Hc Zn	Hc Zn	Hc Zn	Hc Zn	Hc Zn	Hc Zn
	♦Dubhe	REGULUS	PROCYON	♦SIRIUS	RIGEL	ALDEBARAN	♦Mirfak
90	45 39 041	28 03 102	44 01 145	26 30 168	34 48 194	55 35 218	63 46 293
91	46 07 041	28 43 103	44 24 146	26 38 169	34 38 195	55 09 219	63 07 293
92	46 34 041	29 24 104	44 47 147	26 46 170	34 27 196	54 42 221	62 29 293
93	47 01 041	30 04 105	45 09 149	26 53 171	34 14 197	54 14 222	61 51 293
94	47 29 042	30 44 105	45 31 150	26 58 172	34 01 199	53 46 224	61 12 294
95	47 57 042	31 25 106	45 51 151	27 04 173	33 48 200	53 17 225	60 34 294
96	48 25 042	32 04 107	46 11 153	27 08 174	33 33 201	52 47 227	59 56 294
97	48 52 042	32 44 108	46 29 154	27 12 176	33 18 202	52 16 228	59 18 294
98	49 20 042	33 24 109	46 47 155	27 14 177	33 02 203	51 45 229	58 40 294
99	49 48 042	34 03 110	47 04 157	27 17 178	32 45 204	51 13 230	58 02 295
100	50 16 042	34 42 111	47 20 158	27 18 179	32 27 206	50 41 232	57 24 295
101	50 44 042	35 21 111	47 35 160	27 18 180	32 09 207	50 08 233	56 46 295
102	51 12 042	36 00 112	47 49 161	27 18 181	31 50 208	49 34 234	56 09 295
103	51 41 043	36 38 113	48 02 163	27 17 182	31 30 209	49 00 235	55 31 296
104	52 09 043	37 16 114	48 14 164	27 15 183	31 10 210	48 26 236	54 54 296

LAT 46°N

LHA ♈	Hc Zn	Hc Zn	Hc Zn	Hc Zn	Hc Zn	Hc Zn	Hc Zn
	♦DENEB	VEGA	Rasalhague	♦ARCTURUS	REGULUS	♦POLLUX	CAPELLA
206	22 59 048	37 26 070	31 21 105	62 30 164	33 15 251	19 51 290	13 04 325
207	23 30 048	38 05 071	32 01 106	62 41 166	32 36 252	19 12 291	12 41 326
208	24 01 049	38 45 071	32 41 107	62 51 168	31 56 253	18 33 292	12 17 327
209	24 33 049	39 24 072	33 21 108	62 59 170	31 16 254	17 54 292	11 55 327
	DENEB	♦VEGA	Rasalhague	♦ARCTURUS	Denebola	REGULUS	♦Dubhe
210	25 04 050	40 04 072	34 00 109	63 05 172	48 15 232	30 36 255	60 19 318
211	25 36 050	40 43 073	34 40 110	63 10 174	47 42 233	29 56 256	59 52 318
212	26 09 051	41 23 073	35 19 110	63 13 176	47 08 235	29 15 256	59 24 318
213	26 41 051	42 03 074	35 58 111	63 15 178	46 34 236	28 35 257	58 56 318
214	27 14 052	42 43 074	36 37 112	63 16 181	46 00 237	27 54 258	58 28 318
	♦Mirfak	Alpheratz	♦ALTAIR	Rasalhague	♦ARCTURUS	Alkaid	Kochab
285	16 41 033	29 07 077	51 19 160	51 58 215	26 37 271	39 39 304	51 16 337
286	17 04 034	29 47 078	51 32 162	51 33 217	25 55 271	39 04 305	51 00 337
287	17 28 034	30 28 078	51 45 163	51 08 218	25 14 272	38 30 305	50 43 337
288	17 51 035	31 09 079	51 57 165	50 42 220	24 32 273	37 56 305	50 27 337
289	18 15 035	31 50 080	52 07 166	50 15 221	23 50 274	37 22 306	50 11 337
	Mirfak	♦Alpheratz	Enif	ALTAIR	♦Rasalhague	Alphecca	♦Kochab
310	27 44 046	46 21 094	51 21 154	51 19 200	38 36 245	27 58 281	44 31 338
311	28 14 046	47 03 095	51 38 156	51 04 202	37 58 246	27 17 281	44 15 338
312	28 44 047	47 45 096	51 55 157	50 48 203	37 20 247	26 36 282	43 59 338
313	29 15 047	48 26 097	52 10 159	50 31 205	36 41 248	25 55 283	43 43 338
314	29 45 048	49 07 097	52 25 161	50 14 206	36 02 249	25 15 283	43 28 338
	CAPELLA	♦Hamal	Alpheratz	Enif	♦ALTAIR	VEGA	♦Kochab
315	14 22 037	25 42 082	49 49 098	52 38 162	49 55 207	62 46 268	43 12 338
316	14 47 037	26 23 083	50 30 099	52 50 164	49 35 209	62 05 268	42 57 338
317	15 12 038	27 04 084	51 11 100	53 01 165	49 15 210	61 23 269	42 41 338
318	15 38 038	27 46 084	51 52 101	53 11 167	48 53 212	60 41 270	42 26 338
319	16 04 039	28 27 085	52 33 102	53 20 169	48 31 213	60 00 271	42 11 339

LAT 46°

DECLINATION (0°-14°) SAME NAME AS LATITUDE

N. Lat. {LHA greater than 180°........ Zn=Z; LHA less than 180°........... Zn=360−Z}

LHA	0° Hc	d	Z	1° Hc	d	Z	2° Hc	d	Z	3° Hc	d	Z	4° Hc	d	Z
	° ′	′	°	° ′	′	°	° ′	′	°	° ′	′	°	° ′	′	°
0	44 00	+60	180	45 00	+60	180	46 00	+60	180	47 00	+60	180	48 00	+60	180
1	44 00	60	179	45 00	60	179	46 00	60	179	47 00	60	179	48 00	59	179
2	43 58	60	177	44 58	60	177	45 58	60	177	46 58	60	177	47 58	60	177
3	43 56	59	176	44 55	60	176	45 55	60	176	46 55	60	176	47 55	60	176
4	43 52	60	174	44 52	60	174	45 52	60	174	46 52	59	174	47 51	60	174
5	43 47	+60	173	44 47	+60	173	45 47	+60	173	46 47	+60	173	47 47	+59	173
6	43 42	60	172	44 42	59	172	45 41	60	171	46 41	60	171	47 41	59	171
7	43 35	60	170	44 35	60	170	45 35	59	170	46 34	60	170	47 34	59	170
8	43 28	59	169	44 27	60	169	45 27	59	169	46 26	60	168	47 26	59	168
9	43 19	60	168	44 19	59	167	45 18	59	167	46 17	60	167	47 17	59	167
10	43 10	+59	166	44 09	+59	166	45 08	+59	166	46 07	+59	166	47 06	+59	165
11	43 00	59	165	43 59	59	165	44 58	58	164	45 56	59	164	46 55	59	164
12	42 48	59	164	43 47	59	163	44 46	59	163	45 45	58	163	46 43	59	162
13	42 36	59	162	43 35	58	162	44 33	59	162	45 32	58	161	46 30	59	161
14	42 23	58	161	43 21	59	161	44 20	58	160	45 18	58	160	46 16	58	160
15	42 09	+58	160	43 07	+58	159	44 05	+58	159	45 03	+58	159	46 01	+58	158
16	41 54	58	158	42 52	57	158	43 49	58	158	44 47	58	157	45 45	58	157
17	41 38	57	157	42 35	58	157	43 33	58	156	44 31	57	156	45 28	58	155
18	41 21	58	156	42 19	57	155	43 16	57	155	44 13	57	155	45 10	57	154
19	41 03	58	154	42 01	57	154	42 58	57	154	43 55	57	153	44 52	57	153
20	40 45	+57	153	41 42	+57	153	42 39	+57	152	43 36	+56	152	44 32	+57	151
21	40 26	57	152	41 23	56	152	42 19	56	151	43 15	57	151	44 12	56	150
22	40 06	56	151	41 02	56	150	41 58	57	150	42 55	56	149	43 51	56	149
23	39 45	56	150	40 41	56	149	41 37	56	149	42 33	56	148	43 29	55	148
24	39 23	56	148	40 19	56	148	41 15	55	147	42 10	56	147	43 06	55	146
25	39 01	+56	147	39 57	+55	147	40 52	+55	146	41 47	+55	146	42 42	+55	145
26	38 38	55	146	39 33	55	145	40 28	55	145	41 23	55	144	42 18	55	144
27	38 14	55	145	39 09	55	144	40 04	55	144	40 59	54	143	41 53	54	143
28	37 50	55	144	38 45	54	143	39 39	54	143	40 33	54	142	41 27	54	141
29	37 25	54	142	38 19	54	142	39 13	54	141	40 07	54	141	41 01	54	140
30	36 59	+54	141	37 53	+54	141	38 47	+53	140	39 40	+54	140	40 34	+53	139
31	36 33	53	140	37 26	54	140	38 20	53	139	39 13	53	138	40 06	53	138
32	36 06	53	139	36 59	53	138	37 52	53	138	38 45	53	137	39 38	53	137
33	35 38	53	138	36 31	53	137	37 24	53	137	38 17	52	136	39 09	52	136
34	35 10	53	137	36 03	52	136	36 55	52	136	37 47	53	135	38 40	51	134
35	34 41	+52	136	35 33	+53	135	36 26	+52	135	37 18	+51	134	38 09	+52	133
36	34 12	52	135	35 04	52	134	35 56	51	134	36 47	52	133	37 39	51	132
37	33 42	52	134	34 34	51	133	35 25	52	132	36 17	51	132	37 08	51	131
38	33 11	52	133	34 03	51	132	34 54	51	131	35 45	51	131	36 36	51	130
39	32 40	52	132	33 32	51	131	34 23	50	130	35 13	51	130	36 04	50	129
40	32 09	+51	131	33 00	+51	130	33 51	+50	129	34 41	+50	129	35 31	+50	128
41	31 37	51	130	32 28	50	129	33 18	50	128	34 08	50	128	34 58	50	127
42	31 05	50	129	31 55	50	128	32 45	50	127	33 35	50	127	34 25	49	126
43	30 32	50	128	31 22	50	127	32 12	49	126	33 01	50	126	33 51	49	125
44	29 59	50	127	30 49	49	126	31 38	49	125	32 27	50	125	33 17	48	124
45	29 25	+50	126	30 15	+49	125	31 04	+49	124	31 53	+49	124	32 42	+48	123
46	28 51	49	125	29 40	49	124	30 29	49	124	31 18	49	123	32 07	48	122
47	28 17	49	124	29 06	48	123	29 54	49	123	30 43	48	122	31 31	48	121
48	27 42	49	123	28 31	48	122	29 19	48	122	30 07	48	121	30 55	48	120
49	27 07	48	122	27 55	48	121	28 43	48	121	29 31	48	120	30 19	48	119
50	26 31	+48	121	27 19	+48	120	28 07	+48	120	28 55	+48	119	29 43	+47	118
51	25 55	48	120	26 43	48	120	27 31	48	119	28 19	47	118	29 06	47	118
52	25 19	48	119	26 07	47	119	26 54	48	118	27 42	47	117	28 29	47	117
53	24 43	47	119	25 30	47	118	26 17	47	117	27 04	47	116	27 51	47	116
54	24 06	47	118	24 53	47	117	25 40	47	116	26 27	47	116	27 14	46	115
55	23 29	+47	117	24 16	+47	116	25 03	+46	115	25 49	+47	115	26 36	+46	114
56	22 52	46	116	23 38	47	115	24 25	46	115	25 11	46	114	25 57	46	113
57	22 14	46	115	23 00	47	114	23 47	46	114	24 33	46	113	25 19	46	112
58	21 36	46	114	22 22	47	114	23 09	45	113	23 54	46	112	24 40	46	111
59	20 58	46	113	21 44	46	113	22 30	46	112	23 16	45	111	24 01	46	111
60	20 19	+46	113	21 05	+46	112	21 51	+46	111	22 37	+45	111	23 22	+45	110
61	19 41	46	112	20 27	45	111	21 12	46	110	21 58	45	110	22 43	45	109
62	19 02	46	111	19 48	45	110	20 33	45	110	21 18	45	109	22 03	45	108
63	18 23	45	110	19 08	46	109	19 54	45	109	20 39	45	108	21 24	44	107
64	17 44	45	109	18 29	45	109	19 14	45	108	19 59	45	107	20 44	44	107
65	17 04	+45	109	17 49	+45	108	18 34	+45	107	19 19	+45	106	20 04	+44	106
66	16 25	45	108	17 10	44	107	17 54	45	106	18 39	45	106	19 24	44	105
67	15 45	45	107	16 30	44	106	17 14	45	106	17 59	44	105	18 43	44	104
68	15 05	45	106	15 50	44	106	16 34	45	105	17 19	44	104	18 03	44	103
69	14 25	44	105	15 09	45	105	15 54	44	104	16 38	44	103	17 22	44	103

LHA	5° Hc	d	Z	6° Hc	d	Z	7° Hc	d	Z	8° Hc	d	Z	9° Hc	d	Z
	° ′	′	°	° ′	′	°	° ′	′	°	° ′	′	°	° ′	′	°
0	49 00	+60	180	50 00	+60	180	51 00	+60	180	52 00	+60	180	53 00	+60	180
1	48 59	60	179	49 59	60	179	50 59	60	178	51 59	60	178	52 59	60	178
2	48 58	60	177	49 58	60	177	50 58	60	177	51 58	60	177	52 58	60	177
3	48 55	60	175	49 55	60	175	50 55	60	175	51 55	60	175	52 55	60	175
4	48 51	60	174	49 51	60	174	50 51	60	174	51 51	60	174	52 51	59	174
5	48 46	+60	172	49 46	+60	172	50 46	+59	172	51 45	+60	172	52 45	+60	172
6	48 40	60	171	49 40	59	171	50 39	60	171	51 39	60	170	52 39	59	170
7	48 33	60	169	49 33	59	169	50 32	60	169	51 32	59	169	52 31	59	169
8	48 25	59	168	49 24	60	168	50 24	59	168	51 23	59	167	52 22	59	167
9	48 16	59	167	49 15	59	166	50 14	59	166	51 13	59	166	52 12	59	165
10	48 05	+59	165	49 04	+59	165	50 03	+59	164	51 02	+59	164	52 01	+59	164
11	47 54	59	164	48 53	59	163	49 52	58	163	50 50	59	163	51 49	59	162
12	47 42	58	162	48 40	59	162	49 39	58	161	50 37	59	161	51 36	58	161
13	47 29	58	161	48 27	58	160	49 25	58	160	50 23	58	160	51 21	59	159
14	47 14	58	159	48 12	58	159	49 10	58	159	50 08	58	158	51 06	58	158
15	46 59	+58	158	47 57	+58	157	48 55	+57	157	49 52	+58	157	50 50	+57	156
16	46 43	57	156	47 40	58	156	48 38	57	156	49 35	57	155	50 32	58	155
17	46 26	57	155	47 23	57	155	48 20	57	154	49 17	57	154	50 14	57	153
18	46 07	57	154	47 04	57	153	48 01	57	153	48 58	57	152	49 55	56	152
19	45 49	56	152	46 45	57	152	47 42	56	151	48 38	57	151	49 35	56	150
20	45 29	+56	151	46 25	+56	150	47 21	+56	150	48 17	+56	149	49 13	+56	149
21	45 08	56	150	46 04	56	149	47 00	56	149	47 56	55	148	48 51	56	148
22	44 47	55	148	45 42	56	148	46 38	55	147	47 33	56	147	48 29	55	146
23	44 24	56	147	45 20	55	146	46 15	55	146	47 10	55	145	48 05	55	145
24	44 01	55	146	44 56	55	145	45 51	55	145	46 46	54	144	47 40	55	143
25	43 37	+55	144	44 32	+55	144	45 27	+54	143	46 21	+54	143	47 15	+54	142
26	43 13	54	143	44 07	54	143	45 01	54	142	45 55	54	141	46 49	54	141
27	42 47	54	142	43 41	54	141	44 35	54	141	45 29	53	140	46 22	54	140
28	42 21	54	141	43 15	54	140	44 09	53	140	45 02	53	139	45 55	53	138
29	41 55	53	140	42 48	53	139	43 41	53	138	44 34	53	138	45 27	52	137
30	41 27	+53	138	42 20	+53	138	43 13	+53	137	44 06	+52	136	44 58	+52	136
31	40 59	53	137	41 52	52	137	42 44	53	136	43 37	52	135	44 29	52	135
32	40 31	52	136	41 23	52	135	42 15	52	135	43 07	52	134	43 59	51	133
33	40 01	52	135	40 53	52	134	41 45	52	134	42 37	51	133	43 28	51	132
34	39 31	52	134	40 23	52	133	41 15	51	132	42 06	51	132	42 57	51	131
35	39 01	+52	133	39 53	+51	132	40 44	+51	131	41 35	+50	131	42 25	+51	130
36	38 30	51	132	39 21	51	131	40 12	51	130	41 03	50	130	41 53	50	129
37	37 59	50	131	38 49	51	130	39 40	50	129	40 30	50	128	41 20	50	128
38	37 27	50	129	38 17	50	129	39 07	50	128	39 57	50	127	40 47	49	127
39	36 54	50	128	37 44	50	128	38 34	50	127	39 24	49	126	40 13	49	126
40	36 21	+50	127	37 11	+50	127	38 01	+49	126	38 50	+49	125	39 39	+49	125
41	35 48	50	126	36 38	49	126	37 27	49	125	38 16	49	124	39 05	48	123
42	35 14	49	125	36 03	49	125	36 52	49	124	37 41	49	123	38 30	48	122
43	34 40	49	124	35 29	49	124	36 18	48	123	37 06	48	122	37 54	48	121
44	34 05	49	123	34 54	48	123	35 42	49	122	36 31	47	121	37 18	48	120
45	33 30	+49	122	34 19	+48	122	35 07	+48	121	35 55	+47	120	36 42	+48	119
46	32 55	48	121	33 43	48	121	34 31	48	120	35 19	47	119	36 06	47	118
47	32 19	48	120	33 07	48	120	33 55	47	119	34 42	47	118	35 29	47	118
48	31 43	48	120	32 31	47	119	33 18	47	118	34 05	47	117	34 52	46	117
49	31 07	47	119	31 54	47	118	32 41	47	117	33 28	46	116	34 14	47	116
50	30 30	+47	118	31 17	+47	117	32 04	+46	116	32 50	+47	116	33 37	+46	115
51	29 53	47	117	30 40	46	116	31 26	47	115	32 13	46	115	32 59	45	114
52	29 16	46	116	30 02	46	115	30 48	47	114	31 35	45	114	32 20	46	113
53	28 38	46	115	29 24	46	114	30 10	46	114	30 56	46	113	31 42	45	112
54	28 00	46	114	28 46	46	113	29 32	46	113	30 18	45	112	31 03	45	111
55	27 22	+46	113	28 08	+45	113	28 53	+46	112	29 39	+45	111	30 24	+45	110
56	26 43	46	112	27 29	46	112	28 15	45	111	29 00	45	110	29 45	45	109
57	26 05	45	112	26 50	46	111	27 36	45	110	28 21	45	109	29 06	44	109
58	25 26	45	111	26 11	45	110	26 56	45	109	27 41	45	109	28 26	44	108
59	24 47	45	110	25 32	45	109	26 17	45	108	27 02	44	108	27 46	44	107
60	24 07	+45	109	24 52	+45	108	25 37	+45	108	26 22	+44	107	27 06	+44	106
61	23 28	45	108	24 13	44	108	24 57	45	107	25 42	44	106	26 26	44	105
62	22 48	45	107	23 33	44	107	24 17	45	106	25 02	44	105	25 46	44	105
63	22 08	45	107	22 53	44	106	23 37	44	105	24 21	44	104	25 05	44	104
64	21 28	45	106	22 13	44	105	22 57	44	104	23 41	44	104	24 25	43	103
65	20 48	+44	105	21 32	+45	104	22 17	+43	104	23 00	+44	103	23 44	+44	102
66	20 08	44	104	20 52	44	104	21 36	44	103	22 20	43	102	23 03	44	101
67	19 27	44	104	20 11	44	103	20 55	44	102	21 39	43	101	22 22	44	101
68	18 47	44	103	19 31	43	102	20 14	44	101	20 58	43	101	21 41	43	100
69	18 06	44	102	18 50	44	101	19 34	43	101	20 17	43	100	21 00	43	99

LHA	10° Hc	d	Z	11° Hc	d	Z	12° Hc	d	Z	13° Hc	d	Z	14° Hc	d	Z	LHA
	° ′	′	°	° ′	′	°	° ′	′	°	° ′	′	°	° ′	′	°	
0	54 00	+60	180	55 00	+60	180	56 00	+60	180	57 00	+60	180	58 00	+60	180	360
1	53 59	60	178	54 59	60	178	55 59	60	178	56 59	60	178	57 59	60	178	359
2	53 58	60	177	54 58	60	177	55 58	59	177	56 57	60	176	57 57	60	176	358
3	53 55	59	175	54 54	60	175	55 54	60	175	56 54	60	175	57 54	60	175	357
4	53 50	60	173	54 50	60	173	55 50	60	173	56 50	59	173	57 49	60	173	356
5	53 45	+60	172	54 45	+59	172	55 44	+60	171	56 44	+59	171	57 43	+60	171	355
6	53 38	60	170	54 38	59	170	55 37	60	170	56 37	59	169	57 36	60	169	354
7	53 30	60	168	54 30	59	168	55 29	59	168	56 28	60	168	57 28	59	167	353
8	53 21	60	167	54 21	59	166	55 20	59	166	56 19	59	166	57 18	59	166	352
9	53 11	59	165	54 10	59	165	55 09	59	165	56 08	59	164	57 07	59	164	351
10	53 00	+59	164	53 59	+58	163	54 57	+59	163	55 56	+59	162	56 55	+58	162	350
11	52 48	58	162	53 46	59	162	54 45	58	161	55 43	58	161	56 41	58	160	349
12	52 34	58	160	53 32	58	160	54 30	59	160	55 29	58	159	56 27	57	159	348
13	52 20	57	159	53 17	58	158	54 15	58	158	55 13	58	157	56 11	57	157	347
14	52 04	58	157	53 02	57	157	53 59	58	156	54 57	57	156	55 54	57	155	346
15	51 47	+58	156	52 45	+57	155	53 42	+57	155	54 39	+57	154	55 36	+57	154	345
16	51 30	57	154	52 27	56	154	53 23	57	153	54 20	57	153	55 17	56	152	344
17	51 11	57	153	52 08	56	152	53 04	57	152	54 01	56	151	54 57	56	150	343
18	50 51	57	151	51 48	56	151	52 44	56	150	53 40	56	150	54 36	55	149	342
19	50 31	56	150	51 27	56	149	52 23	55	149	53 18	56	148	54 14	55	147	341
20	50 09	+56	148	51 05	+55	148	52 00	+56	147	52 56	+55	146	53 51	+54	146	340
21	49 47	55	147	50 42	55	146	51 37	55	146	52 32	55	145	53 27	54	144	339
22	49 24	55	146	50 19	54	145	51 13	55	144	52 08	54	144	53 02	54	143	338
23	49 00	54	144	49 54	54	144	50 48	55	143	51 43	53	142	52 36	54	141	337
24	48 35	54	143	49 29	54	142	50 23	54	141	51 17	53	141	52 10	53	140	336
25	48 09	+54	141	49 03	+53	141	49 56	+54	140	50 50	+53	139	51 43	+52	139	335
26	47 43	53	140	48 36	53	139	49 29	53	139	50 22	53	138	51 15	52	137	334
27	47 16	53	139	48 09	52	138	49 01	53	137	49 54	52	137	50 46	52	136	333
28	46 48	53	138	47 41	52	137	48 33	52	136	49 25	52	135	50 17	51	135	332
29	46 19	53	136	47 12	52	136	48 04	51	135	48 55	52	134	49 47	51	133	331
30	45 50	+52	135	46 42	+52	134	47 34	+51	134	48 25	+51	133	49 16	+51	132	330
31	45 21	51	134	46 12	51	133	47 03	51	132	47 54	51	132	48 45	50	131	329
32	44 50	51	133	45 41	51	132	46 32	51	131	47 23	50	130	48 13	50	130	328
33	44 19	51	131	45 10	50	131	46 00	51	130	46 51	49	129	47 40	50	128	327
34	43 48	50	130	44 38	50	130	45 28	50	129	46 18	49	128	47 07	50	127	326
35	43 16	+50	129	44 06	+49	128	44 55	+50	128	45 45	+49	127	46 34	+49	126	325
36	42 43	50	128	43 33	49	127	44 22	49	127	45 11	49	126	46 00	48	125	324
37	42 10	49	127	42 59	49	126	43 48	49	125	44 37	49	125	45 26	48	124	323
38	41 36	49	126	42 25	49	125	43 14	49	124	44 03	48	123	44 51	47	123	322
39	41 02	49	125	41 51	48	124	42 39	49	123	43 28	47	122	44 15	48	122	321
40	40 28	+48	124	41 16	+48	123	42 04	+48	122	42 52	+48	121	43 40	+47	120	320
41	39 53	48	123	40 41	48	122	41 29	47	121	42 16	47	120	43 03	47	119	319
42	39 18	48	122	40 06	47	121	40 53	47	120	41 40	47	119	42 27	46	118	318
43	38 42	48	121	39 30	47	120	40 17	47	119	41 04	46	118	41 50	46	117	317
44	38 06	47	120	38 53	47	119	39 40	47	118	40 27	46	117	41 13	46	116	316
45	37 30	+47	119	38 17	+46	118	39 03	+46	117	39 49	+46	116	40 35	+46	115	315
46	36 53	47	118	37 40	46	117	38 26	46	116	39 12	46	115	39 58	45	114	314
47	36 16	46	117	37 02	46	116	37 48	46	115	38 34	45	114	39 19	46	114	313
48	35 38	47	116	36 25	45	115	37 10	46	114	37 56	45	113	38 41	45	113	312
49	35 01	46	115	35 47	45	114	36 32	46	113	37 18	45	112	38 03	44	112	311
50	34 23	+45	114	35 08	+46	113	35 54	+45	112	36 39	+45	112	37 24	+44	111	310
51	33 44	46	113	34 30	45	112	35 15	45	111	36 00	45	111	36 45	44	110	309
52	33 06	45	112	33 51	45	111	34 36	45	111	35 21	44	110	36 05	44	109	308
53	32 27	45	111	33 12	45	111	33 57	45	110	34 42	44	109	35 26	43	108	307
54	31 48	45	110	32 33	45	110	33 18	44	109	34 02	44	108	34 46	44	107	306
55	31 09	+45	110	31 54	+44	109	32 38	+44	108	33 22	+44	107	34 06	+43	106	305
56	30 30	44	109	31 14	44	108	31 58	44	107	32 42	44	106	33 26	43	105	304
57	29 50	44	108	30 34	44	107	31 18	44	106	32 02	44	105	32 46	43	105	303
58	29 10	45	107	29 55	43	106	30 38	44	105	31 22	43	105	32 05	43	104	302
59	28 30	44	106	29 14	44	105	29 58	44	105	30 42	43	104	31 25	43	103	301
60	27 50	+44	105	28 34	+44	105	29 18	+43	104	30 01	+43	103	30 44	+43	102	300
61	27 10	44	105	27 54	43	104	28 37	43	103	29 20	43	102	30 03	43	101	299
62	26 30	43	104	27 13	43	103	27 56	44	102	28 40	42	101	29 22	43	101	298
63	25 49	43	103	26 32	44	102	27 16	43	101	27 59	42	101	28 41	43	100	297
64	25 08	44	102	25 52	43	101	26 35	43	101	27 18	42	100	28 00	42	99	296
65	24 28	+43	101	25 11	+43	101	25 54	+42	100	26 36	+43	99	27 19	+42	98	295
66	23 47	43	101	24 30	43	100	25 13	42	99	25 55	43	98	26 38	42	97	294
67	23 06	43	100	23 49	42	99	24 31	43	98	25 14	42	98	25 56	42	97	293
68	22 24	43	99	23 07	43	98	23 50	43	98	24 33	42	97	25 15	42	96	292
69	21 43	43	98	22 26	43	98	23 09	42	97	23 51	42	96	24 33	42	95	291

S. Lat. {LHA greater than 180°........ Zn=180−Z; LHA less than 180°........... Zn=180+Z}

DECLINATION (0°-14°) SAME NAME AS LATITUDE

LAT 46°

LAT 46°

N. Lat. {LHA greater than 180°........ Zn=Z; LHA less than 180°............ Zn=360−Z}

DECLINATION (15°-29°) SAME NAME AS LATITUDE

LHA	15° Hc	d	Z	16° Hc	d	Z	17° Hc	d	Z	18° Hc	d	Z	19° Hc	d	Z
	° ′	′	°	° ′	′	°	° ′	′	°	° ′	′	°	° ′	′	°
0	59 00	+60	180	60 00	+60	180	61 00	+60	180	62 00	+60	180	63 00	+60	180
1	58 59	60	178	59 59	60	178	60 59	60	178	61 59	60	178	62 59	60	178
2	58 57	60	176	59 57	60	176	60 57	60	176	61 57	60	176	62 57	60	176
3	58 54	60	174	59 54	60	174	60 54	59	174	61 53	60	174	62 53	60	174
4	58 49	60	173	59 49	60	172	60 49	59	172	61 48	60	172	62 48	60	172
5	58 43	+60	171	59 43	+59	170	60 42	+60	170	61 42	+59	170	62 41	+60	170
6	58 36	59	169	59 35	59	169	60 34	60	168	61 34	59	168	62 33	59	168
7	58 27	59	167	59 26	59	167	60 25	59	166	61 24	59	166	62 23	59	166
8	58 17	59	165	59 16	59	165	60 15	59	164	61 14	58	164	62 12	59	164
9	58 06	58	163	59 04	59	163	60 03	58	163	61 01	59	162	62 00	58	162
10	57 53	+58	162	58 51	+59	161	59 50	+58	161	60 48	+58	160	61 46	+58	160
11	57 39	58	160	58 37	58	159	59 35	58	159	60 33	58	158	61 31	57	158
12	57 24	58	158	58 22	58	158	59 20	57	157	60 17	58	157	61 15	57	156
13	57 08	58	156	58 06	57	156	59 03	57	155	60 00	57	155	60 57	57	154
14	56 51	57	155	57 48	57	154	58 45	57	154	59 42	56	153	60 38	56	152
15	56 33	+56	153	57 29	+57	152	58 26	+56	152	59 22	+56	151	60 18	+56	150
16	56 13	56	151	57 09	56	151	58 05	56	150	59 01	56	149	59 57	55	149
17	55 53	56	150	56 49	55	149	57 44	56	148	58 40	55	148	59 35	54	147
18	55 31	56	148	56 27	55	148	57 22	55	147	58 17	54	146	59 11	55	145
19	55 09	55	147	56 04	55	146	56 59	54	145	57 53	54	144	58 47	54	144
20	54 45	+55	145	55 40	+54	144	56 34	+54	144	57 28	+54	143	58 22	+53	142
21	54 21	54	144	55 15	54	143	56 09	54	142	57 03	53	141	57 56	53	140
22	53 56	54	142	54 50	53	141	55 43	53	141	56 36	53	140	57 29	52	139
23	53 30	53	141	54 23	53	140	55 16	53	139	56 09	52	138	57 01	52	137
24	53 03	53	139	53 56	52	138	54 48	52	138	55 40	52	137	56 32	51	136
25	52 35	+53	138	53 28	+52	137	54 20	+51	136	55 11	+52	135	56 03	+51	134
26	52 07	52	136	52 59	52	136	53 51	51	135	54 42	51	134	55 33	50	133
27	51 38	51	135	52 29	52	134	53 21	50	133	54 11	51	132	55 02	50	132
28	51 08	51	134	51 59	51	133	52 50	50	132	53 40	50	131	54 30	50	130
29	50 38	50	132	51 28	51	132	52 19	50	131	53 09	49	130	53 58	49	129
30	50 07	+50	131	50 57	+50	130	51 47	+49	129	52 36	+49	129	53 25	+49	128
31	49 35	50	130	50 25	49	129	51 14	49	128	52 03	49	127	52 52	48	126
32	49 03	49	129	49 52	49	128	50 41	49	127	51 30	48	126	52 18	48	125
33	48 30	49	127	49 19	49	127	50 08	48	126	50 56	48	125	51 44	47	124
34	47 57	48	126	48 45	48	125	49 33	48	125	50 21	48	124	51 09	47	123
35	47 23	+48	125	48 11	+48	124	48 59	+47	123	49 46	+47	122	50 33	+47	121
36	46 48	48	124	47 36	48	123	48 24	47	122	49 11	46	121	49 57	47	120
37	46 14	47	123	47 01	47	122	47 48	47	121	48 35	46	120	49 21	46	119
38	45 38	48	122	46 26	46	121	47 12	47	120	47 59	46	119	48 45	45	118
39	45 03	47	121	45 50	46	120	46 36	46	119	47 22	46	118	48 08	45	117
40	44 27	+46	120	45 13	+46	119	45 59	+46	118	46 45	+45	117	47 30	+45	116
41	43 50	46	119	44 36	46	118	45 22	46	117	46 08	45	116	46 53	44	115
42	43 13	46	118	43 59	46	117	44 45	45	116	45 30	45	115	46 15	44	114
43	42 36	46	117	43 22	45	116	44 07	45	115	44 52	44	114	45 36	44	113
44	41 59	45	116	42 44	45	115	43 29	45	114	44 14	44	113	44 58	44	112
45	41 21	+45	115	42 06	+45	114	42 51	+44	113	43 35	+44	112	44 19	+43	111
46	40 43	45	114	41 28	44	113	42 12	44	112	42 56	44	111	43 40	43	110
47	40 05	44	113	40 49	44	112	41 33	44	111	42 17	44	110	43 01	43	109
48	39 26	44	112	40 10	44	111	40 54	44	110	41 38	43	109	42 21	43	108
49	38 47	44	111	39 31	44	110	40 15	44	109	40 59	42	108	41 41	43	107
50	38 08	+44	110	38 52	+44	109	39 36	+43	108	40 19	+43	107	41 02	+42	106
51	37 29	43	109	38 12	44	108	38 56	43	107	39 39	42	106	40 21	43	105
52	36 49	44	108	37 33	43	107	38 16	43	106	38 59	42	105	39 41	42	105
53	36 09	44	107	36 53	43	106	37 36	43	105	38 19	42	105	39 01	42	104
54	35 30	43	106	36 13	43	106	36 56	42	105	37 38	42	104	38 20	42	103
55	34 49	+43	106	35 32	+43	105	36 15	+43	104	36 58	+41	103	37 39	+42	102
56	34 09	43	105	34 52	43	104	35 35	42	103	36 17	42	102	36 59	41	101
57	33 29	43	104	34 12	42	103	34 54	42	102	35 36	42	101	36 18	41	100
58	32 48	43	103	33 31	42	102	34 13	42	101	34 55	42	100	35 37	41	100
59	32 08	42	102	32 50	42	101	33 32	42	101	34 14	41	100	34 55	41	99
60	31 27	+42	101	32 09	+42	101	32 51	+42	100	33 33	+41	99	34 14	+41	98
61	30 46	42	101	31 28	42	100	32 10	42	99	32 52	41	98	33 33	41	97
62	30 05	42	100	30 47	42	99	31 29	41	98	32 10	41	97	32 51	41	96
63	29 24	42	99	30 06	41	98	30 47	42	97	31 29	41	97	32 10	41	96
64	28 42	42	98	29 24	42	97	30 06	41	97	30 47	42	96	31 29	40	95
65	28 01	+42	97	28 43	+42	97	29 25	+41	96	30 06	+41	95	30 47	+41	94
66	27 20	42	97	28 02	41	96	28 43	41	95	29 24	41	94	30 05	41	93
67	26 38	42	96	27 20	42	95	28 02	41	94	28 43	41	93	29 24	40	93
68	25 57	42	95	26 39	41	94	27 20	41	94	28 01	41	93	28 42	41	92
69	25 15	42	94	25 57	41	94	26 38	42	93	27 20	40	92	28 00	41	91

LHA	20° Hc	d	Z	21° Hc	d	Z	22° Hc	d	Z	23° Hc	d	Z	24° Hc	d	Z
	° ′	′	°	° ′	′	°	° ′	′	°	° ′	′	°	° ′	′	°
0	64 00	+60	180	65 00	+60	180	66 00	+60	180	67 00	+60	180	68 00	+60	180
1	63 59	60	178	64 59	60	178	65 59	60	178	66 59	60	178	67 59	60	178
2	63 57	60	176	64 57	60	176	65 57	60	175	66 57	60	175	67 57	59	175
3	63 53	60	174	64 53	60	173	65 53	59	173	66 52	60	173	67 52	60	173
4	63 48	59	172	64 47	60	171	65 47	59	171	66 46	60	171	67 46	59	170
5	63 41	+59	169	64 40	+59	169	65 39	+60	169	66 39	+59	168	67 38	+59	168
6	63 32	59	167	64 31	60	167	65 31	59	167	66 30	59	166	67 29	58	166
7	63 22	59	165	64 21	59	165	65 20	59	164	66 19	58	164	67 17	59	163
8	63 11	59	163	64 10	58	163	65 08	58	162	66 06	58	162	67 04	59	161
9	62 58	58	161	63 56	58	161	64 54	58	160	65 52	58	159	66 50	58	159
10	62 44	+58	159	63 42	+57	159	64 39	+58	158	65 37	+57	157	66 34	+57	157
11	62 28	58	157	63 26	57	157	64 23	57	156	65 20	57	155	66 17	56	154
12	62 12	57	155	63 09	56	155	64 05	57	154	65 02	56	153	65 58	56	152
13	61 54	56	153	62 50	56	153	63 46	56	152	64 42	56	151	65 38	55	150
14	61 34	56	152	62 30	56	151	63 26	55	150	64 21	56	149	65 17	54	148
15	61 14	+55	150	62 09	+56	149	63 05	+54	148	63 59	+55	147	64 54	+54	146
16	60 52	55	148	61 47	55	147	62 42	54	146	63 36	54	145	64 30	54	144
17	60 29	55	146	61 24	54	145	62 18	54	144	63 12	53	143	64 05	53	142
18	60 06	54	144	61 00	53	144	61 53	53	143	62 46	53	142	63 39	52	141
19	59 41	53	143	60 34	53	142	61 27	53	141	62 20	52	140	63 12	52	139
20	59 15	+53	141	60 08	+53	140	61 01	+52	139	61 53	+51	138	62 44	+51	137
21	58 49	52	139	59 41	52	139	60 33	51	138	61 24	51	136	62 15	51	135
22	58 21	52	138	59 13	51	137	60 04	51	136	60 55	51	135	61 46	49	134
23	57 53	51	136	58 44	51	135	59 35	50	134	60 25	50	133	61 15	49	132
24	57 23	51	135	58 14	51	134	59 05	50	133	59 55	49	132	60 44	48	131
25	56 54	+50	133	57 44	+50	132	58 34	+49	131	59 23	+49	130	60 12	+48	129
26	56 23	50	132	57 13	49	131	58 02	49	130	58 51	48	129	59 39	48	128
27	55 52	49	131	56 41	49	130	57 30	48	128	58 18	48	127	59 06	47	126
28	55 20	48	129	56 08	49	128	56 57	48	127	57 45	47	126	58 32	46	125
29	54 47	48	128	55 35	48	127	56 23	48	126	57 11	46	125	57 57	46	123
30	54 14	+48	127	55 02	+47	126	55 49	+47	124	56 36	+46	123	57 22	+46	122
31	53 40	47	125	54 27	47	124	55 14	47	123	56 01	46	122	56 47	45	121
32	53 06	47	124	53 53	46	123	54 39	46	122	55 25	46	121	56 11	44	120
33	52 31	47	123	53 18	46	122	54 04	45	121	54 49	45	120	55 34	44	118
34	51 56	46	122	52 42	46	121	53 28	45	119	54 13	44	118	54 57	44	117
35	51 20	+46	120	52 06	+45	119	52 51	+45	118	53 36	+44	117	54 20	+43	116
36	50 44	45	119	51 29	45	118	52 14	45	117	52 59	43	116	53 42	43	115
37	50 07	45	118	50 52	45	117	51 37	44	116	52 21	43	115	53 04	43	114
38	49 30	45	117	50 15	44	116	50 59	44	115	51 43	43	114	52 26	43	113
39	48 53	44	116	49 37	44	115	50 21	44	114	51 05	43	113	51 48	42	112
40	48 15	+44	115	48 59	+44	114	49 43	+43	113	50 26	+43	112	51 09	+41	111
41	47 37	44	114	48 21	44	113	49 05	42	112	49 47	42	111	50 29	42	110
42	46 59	44	113	47 43	43	112	48 26	42	111	49 08	42	110	49 50	41	109
43	46 20	44	112	47 04	43	111	47 47	42	110	48 29	42	109	49 11	41	108
44	45 42	43	111	46 25	42	110	47 07	42	109	47 49	42	108	48 31	40	107
45	45 02	+43	110	45 45	+43	109	46 28	+41	108	47 09	+42	107	47 51	+40	106
46	44 23	43	109	45 06	42	108	45 48	41	107	46 29	41	106	47 10	41	105
47	43 44	42	108	44 26	42	107	45 08	41	106	45 49	41	105	46 30	40	104
48	43 04	42	107	43 46	42	106	44 28	41	105	45 09	41	104	45 50	40	103
49	42 24	42	106	43 06	41	105	43 47	41	104	44 28	41	103	45 09	40	102
50	41 44	+42	105	42 26	+41	104	43 07	+41	103	43 48	+40	102	44 28	+40	101
51	41 04	41	104	41 45	41	104	42 26	41	103	43 07	40	102	43 47	40	101
52	40 23	42	104	41 05	41	103	41 46	40	102	42 26	40	101	43 06	40	100
53	39 43	41	103	40 24	41	102	41 05	40	101	41 45	40	100	42 25	39	99
54	39 02	41	102	39 43	41	101	40 24	40	100	41 04	40	99	41 44	39	98
55	38 21	+41	101	39 02	+41	100	39 43	+40	99	40 23	+39	98	41 02	+40	97
56	37 40	41	100	38 21	40	99	39 01	40	98	39 41	40	97	40 21	39	96
57	36 59	41	99	37 40	40	99	38 20	40	98	39 00	40	97	39 40	39	96
58	36 18	40	99	36 58	41	98	37 39	40	97	38 19	39	96	38 58	39	95
59	35 36	41	98	36 17	40	97	36 57	40	96	37 37	40	95	38 17	38	94
60	34 55	+41	97	35 36	+40	96	36 16	+40	95	36 56	+39	94	37 35	+39	93
61	34 14	40	96	34 54	40	95	35 34	40	95	36 14	39	94	36 53	39	93
62	33 32	41	96	34 13	40	95	34 53	39	94	35 32	40	93	36 12	38	92
63	32 51	40	95	33 31	40	94	34 11	40	93	34 51	39	92	35 30	39	91
64	32 09	41	94	32 50	40	93	33 30	39	92	34 09	39	91	34 48	39	90
65	31 28	+40	93	32 08	+40	92	32 48	+39	92	33 27	+40	91	34 07	+38	90
66	30 46	40	93	31 26	40	92	32 06	40	91	32 46	39	90	33 25	39	89
67	30 04	41	92	30 45	40	91	31 25	39	90	32 04	39	89	32 43	39	88
68	29 23	40	91	30 03	40	90	30 43	39	89	31 22	40	88	32 02	38	88
69	28 41	40	90	29 21	40	90	30 01	40	89	30 41	39	88	31 20	39	87

LHA	25° Hc	d	Z	26° Hc	d	Z	27° Hc	d	Z	28° Hc	d	Z	29° Hc	d	Z	LHA
	° ′	′	°	° ′	′	°	° ′	′	°	° ′	′	°	° ′	′	°	
0	69 00	+60	180	70 00	+60	180	71 00	+60	180	72 00	+60	180	73 00	+60	180	360
1	68 59	60	178	69 59	60	177	70 59	60	177	71 59	60	177	72 59	60	177	359
2	68 56	60	175	69 56	60	175	70 56	60	175	71 56	60	174	72 56	59	174	358
3	68 52	59	172	69 51	60	172	70 51	60	172	71 51	59	172	72 50	60	171	357
4	68 45	60	170	69 45	59	170	70 44	60	169	71 44	59	169	72 43	59	168	356
5	68 37	+59	168	69 36	+59	167	70 35	+59	167	71 34	+59	166	72 33	+59	165	355
6	68 27	59	165	69 26	59	165	70 25	58	164	71 23	59	163	72 22	58	162	354
7	68 16	58	163	69 14	58	162	70 12	58	161	71 10	58	161	72 08	58	160	353
8	68 03	57	160	69 00	58	160	69 58	58	159	70 56	57	158	71 53	57	157	352
9	67 48	57	158	68 45	57	157	69 42	57	156	70 39	56	155	71 35	57	154	351
10	67 31	+57	156	68 28	+57	155	69 25	+56	154	70 21	+56	153	71 17	+55	152	350
11	67 13	57	154	68 10	55	153	69 05	56	152	70 01	55	151	70 56	55	149	349
12	66 54	56	151	67 50	55	150	68 45	55	149	69 40	54	148	70 34	54	147	348
13	66 33	55	149	67 28	55	148	68 23	54	147	69 17	54	146	70 11	52	145	347
14	66 11	55	147	67 06	54	146	68 00	53	145	68 53	53	144	69 46	52	142	346
15	65 48	+54	145	66 42	+53	144	67 35	+53	143	68 28	+52	142	69 20	+51	140	345
16	65 24	53	143	66 17	52	142	67 09	52	141	68 01	51	139	68 52	51	138	344
17	64 58	52	141	65 50	52	140	66 42	51	139	67 33	51	138	68 24	49	136	343
18	64 31	52	139	65 23	51	138	66 14	51	137	67 05	49	136	67 54	49	134	342
19	64 04	51	138	64 55	50	136	65 45	50	135	66 35	49	134	67 24	48	132	341
20	63 35	+51	136	64 26	+49	135	65 15	+49	133	66 04	+49	132	66 53	+47	130	340
21	63 06	50	134	63 56	49	133	64 45	48	132	65 33	48	130	66 21	46	129	339
22	62 35	50	133	63 25	48	131	64 13	48	130	65 01	47	129	65 48	45	127	338
23	62 04	49	131	62 53	48	130	63 41	47	128	64 28	46	127	65 14	45	125	337
24	61 32	48	129	62 20	48	128	63 08	46	127	63 54	46	125	64 40	44	124	336
25	61 00	+47	128	61 47	+47	127	62 34	+46	125	63 20	+45	124	64 05	+44	122	335
26	60 27	46	126	61 13	47	125	62 00	45	124	62 45	44	122	63 29	44	121	334
27	59 53	46	125	60 39	46	124	61 25	44	122	62 09	44	121	62 53	43	119	333
28	59 18	46	124	60 04	45	122	60 49	44	121	61 33	44	120	62 17	42	118	332
29	58 43	46	122	59 29	44	121	60 13	44	120	60 57	43	118	61 40	41	117	331
30	58 08	+45	121	58 53	+44	120	59 37	+43	118	60 20	+42	117	61 02	+41	115	330
31	57 32	44	120	58 16	44	118	59 00	42	117	59 42	42	116	60 24	41	114	329
32	56 55	44	118	57 39	43	117	58 22	43	116	59 05	41	114	59 46	41	113	328
33	56 18	44	117	57 02	43	116	57 45	42	115	58 27	41	113	59 08	40	112	327
34	55 41	43	116	56 24	43	115	57 07	41	113	57 48	41	112	58 29	39	111	326
35	55 03	+43	115	55 46	+42	114	56 28	+41	112	57 09	+41	111	57 50	+39	110	325
36	54 25	43	114	55 08	41	113	55 49	41	111	56 30	40	110	57 10	39	109	324
37	53 47	42	113	54 29	41	111	55 10	41	110	55 51	40	109	56 31	38	108	323
38	53 09	41	112	53 50	41	110	54 31	40	109	55 11	40	108	55 51	38	107	322
39	52 30	41	111	53 11	41	109	53 52	40	108	54 32	39	107	55 11	38	106	321
40	51 50	+42	110	52 32	+40	108	53 12	+40	107	53 52	+38	106	54 30	+38	105	320
41	51 11	41	109	51 52	40	107	52 32	39	106	53 11	39	105	53 50	38	104	319
42	50 31	41	108	51 12	40	106	51 52	39	105	52 31	38	104	53 09	38	103	318
43	49 52	40	107	50 32	40	105	51 12	38	104	51 50	39	103	52 29	37	102	317
44	49 11	41	106	49 52	39	104	50 31	39	103	51 10	38	102	51 48	37	101	316
45	48 31	+40	105	49 11	+39	104	49 50	+39	102	50 29	+38	101	51 07	+37	100	315
46	47 51	40	104	48 31	39	103	49 10	38	102	49 48	38	100	50 26	36	99	314
47	47 10	40	103	47 50	39	102	48 29	38	101	49 07	37	99	49 44	37	98	313
48	46 30	39	102	47 09	39	101	47 48	38	100	48 26	37	99	49 03	37	97	312
49	45 49	39	101	46 28	39	100	47 07	37	99	47 44	38	98	48 22	36	97	311
50	45 08	+39	100	45 47	+38	99	46 25	+38	98	47 03	+37	97	47 40	+37	96	310
51	44 27	39	99	45 06	38	98	45 44	38	97	46 22	37	96	46 59	36	95	309
52	43 46	38	99	44 24	39	98	45 03	37	96	45 40	37	95	46 17	36	94	308
53	43 04	39	98	43 43	38	97	44 21	38	96	44 59	37	95	45 36	36	93	307
54	42 23	39	97	43 02	38	96	43 40	37	95	44 17	37	94	44 54	36	93	306
55	41 42	+38	96	42 20	+38	95	42 58	+38	94	43 36	+36	93	44 12	+37	92	305
56	41 00	39	95	41 39	38	94	42 17	37	93	42 54	37	92	43 31	36	91	304
57	40 19	38	95	40 57	38	94	41 35	37	93	42 12	37	92	42 49	36	91	303
58	39 37	38	94	40 15	38	93	40 53	38	92	41 31	36	91	42 07	36	90	302
59	38 55	39	93	39 34	38	92	40 12	37	91	40 49	37	90	41 26	36	89	301
60	38 14	+38	92	38 52	+38	91	39 30	+37	90	40 07	+37	89	40 44	+36	88	300
61	37 32	38	92	38 10	38	91	38 48	38	90	39 26	36	89	40 02	37	88	299
62	36 50	39	91	37 29	38	90	38 07	37	89	38 44	37	88	39 21	36	87	298
63	36 09	38	90	36 47	38	89	37 25	37	88	38 02	37	87	38 39	36	86	297
64	35 27	38	90	36 05	38	89	36 43	38	88	37 21	37	87	37 58	36	86	296
65	34 45	+39	89	35 24	+38	88	36 02	+37	87	36 39	+37	86	37 16	+36	85	295
66	34 04	38	88	34 42	38	87	35 20	37	86	35 57	37	85	36 34	37	84	294
67	33 22	38	87	34 00	38	86	34 38	38	86	35 16	37	85	35 53	37	84	293
68	32 40	39	87	33 19	38	86	33 57	38	85	34 35	37	84	35 12	36	83	292
69	31 59	38	86	32 37	38	85	33 15	38	84	33 53	37	83	34 30	37	82	291

15° 16° 17° 18° 19° 20° 21° 22° 23° 24° 25° 26° 27° 28° 29°

S. Lat. {LHA greater than 180°........ Zn=180−Z; LHA less than 180°............ Zn=180+Z}

DECLINATION (15°-29°) SAME NAME AS LATITUDE

LAT 46°

LAT 46°

DECLINATION (15°-29°) SAME NAME AS LATITUDE

LAT 46°

N. Lat. {LHA greater than 180°........ Zn=Z; LHA less than 180°.......... Zn=360−Z}

LHA	15° Hc	d	Z	16° Hc	d	Z	17° Hc	d	Z	18° Hc	d	Z	19° Hc	d	Z	20° Hc	d	Z	21° Hc	d	Z	22° Hc	d	Z	23° Hc	d	Z	24° Hc	d	Z	25° Hc	d	Z	26° Hc	d	Z	27° Hc	d	Z	28° Hc	d	Z	29° Hc	d	Z	LHA
	° ′	′	°	° ′	′	°	° ′	′	°	° ′	′	°	° ′	′	°	° ′	′	°	° ′	′	°	° ′	′	°	° ′	′	°	° ′	′	°	° ′	′	°	° ′	′	°	° ′	′	°	° ′	′	°	° ′	′	°	
70	24 34	+41	94	25 15	+42	93	25 57	+41	92	26 38	+41	91	27 19	+40	90	27 59	+41	90	28 40	+40	89	29 20	+39	88	29 59	+39	87	30 38	+39	86	31 17	+39	85	31 56	+38	84	32 34	+38	83	33 12	+37	83	33 49	+37	82	290
71	23 52	42	93	24 34	41	92	25 15	41	91	25 56	41	91	26 37	41	90	27 18	40	89	27 58	40	88	28 38	40	87	29 18	39	86	29 57	39	86	30 36	38	85	31 14	39	84	31 53	37	83	32 30	38	82	33 08	37	81	289
72	23 10	42	92	23 52	41	91	24 33	42	91	25 15	40	90	25 55	41	89	26 36	40	88	27 16	40	87	27 56	40	87	28 36	39	86	29 15	39	85	29 54	39	84	30 33	38	83	31 11	38	82	31 49	38	81	32 27	37	80	288
73	22 29	41	91	23 10	42	91	23 52	41	90	24 33	41	89	25 14	40	88	25 54	41	88	26 35	40	87	27 15	39	86	27 54	40	85	28 34	39	84	29 13	39	83	29 52	38	82	30 30	38	82	31 08	38	81	31 46	37	80	287
74	21 47	42	91	22 29	41	90	23 10	41	89	23 51	41	88	24 32	41	88	25 13	40	87	25 53	40	86	26 33	40	85	27 13	39	84	27 52	40	83	28 32	38	83	29 10	39	82	29 49	38	81	30 27	38	80	31 05	37	79	286
75	21 05	+42	90	21 47	+41	89	22 28	+42	88	23 10	+40	88	23 50	+41	87	24 31	+41	86	25 12	+40	85	25 52	+39	84	26 31	+40	84	27 11	+39	83	27 50	+39	82	28 29	+39	81	29 08	+38	80	29 46	+38	79	30 24	+37	78	285
76	20 24	41	89	21 05	42	89	21 47	41	88	22 28	41	87	23 09	41	86	23 50	40	85	24 30	40	85	25 10	40	84	25 50	40	83	26 30	39	82	27 09	39	81	27 48	39	80	28 27	38	80	29 05	38	79	29 43	38	78	284
77	19 42	42	89	20 24	41	88	21 05	41	87	21 46	41	86	22 27	41	86	23 08	41	85	23 49	40	84	24 29	40	83	25 09	39	82	25 48	40	81	26 28	39	81	27 07	39	80	27 46	38	79	28 24	38	78	29 02	38	77	283
78	19 00	42	88	19 42	42	87	20 24	41	86	21 05	41	86	21 46	41	85	22 27	40	84	23 07	40	83	23 47	40	82	24 27	40	82	25 07	40	81	25 47	39	80	26 26	39	79	27 05	39	78	27 44	38	77	28 22	38	77	282
79	18 19	41	87	19 00	42	86	19 42	41	86	20 23	41	85	21 04	41	84	21 45	41	83	22 26	40	83	23 06	40	82	23 46	40	81	24 26	40	80	25 06	39	79	25 45	39	78	26 24	39	78	27 03	38	77	27 41	38	76	281
80	17 37	+42	86	18 19	+41	86	19 00	+42	85	19 42	+41	84	20 23	+41	83	21 04	+40	83	21 44	+41	82	22 25	+40	81	23 05	+40	80	23 45	+40	79	24 25	+39	79	25 04	+40	78	25 44	+38	77	26 22	+39	76	27 01	+38	75	280
81	16 56	41	86	17 37	42	85	18 19	41	84	19 00	41	84	19 41	41	83	20 22	41	82	21 03	41	81	21 44	40	80	22 24	40	80	23 04	40	79	23 44	40	78	24 24	39	77	25 03	39	76	25 42	39	75	26 21	38	75	279
82	16 14	42	85	16 56	41	84	17 37	42	84	18 19	41	83	19 00	41	82	19 41	41	81	20 22	41	81	21 03	40	80	21 43	40	79	22 23	40	78	23 03	40	77	23 43	40	76	24 23	39	76	25 02	39	75	25 41	38	74	278
83	15 33	41	84	16 14	42	84	16 56	42	83	17 38	41	82	18 19	41	81	19 00	41	81	19 41	41	80	20 22	40	79	21 02	41	78	21 43	40	77	22 23	40	77	23 03	39	76	23 42	40	75	24 22	39	74	25 01	38	73	277
84	14 51	42	84	15 33	42	83	16 15	41	82	16 56	42	81	17 38	41	81	18 19	41	80	19 00	41	79	19 41	41	78	20 22	40	78	21 02	40	77	21 42	40	76	22 22	40	75	23 02	40	74	23 42	39	74	24 21	39	73	276
85	14 10	+42	83	14 52	+42	82	15 34	+41	82	16 15	+42	81	16 57	+41	80	17 38	+41	79	18 19	+41	78	19 00	+41	78	19 41	+41	77	20 22	+40	76	21 02	+40	75	21 42	+40	75	22 22	+40	74	23 02	+39	73	23 41	+39	72	275
86	13 28	42	82	14 10	42	82	14 52	42	81	15 34	42	80	16 16	41	79	16 57	41	79	17 38	42	78	18 20	40	77	19 00	41	76	19 41	41	75	20 22	40	75	21 02	40	74	21 42	40	73	22 22	40	72	23 02	39	71	274
87	12 47	42	82	13 29	42	81	14 11	42	80	14 53	42	79	15 35	41	79	16 16	42	78	16 58	41	77	17 39	41	76	18 20	41	76	19 01	41	75	19 42	40	74	20 22	40	73	21 02	40	72	21 42	40	72	22 22	40	71	273
88	12 06	42	81	12 48	42	80	13 30	42	79	14 12	42	79	14 54	42	78	15 36	41	77	16 17	42	76	16 59	41	76	17 40	41	75	18 21	41	74	19 02	40	73	19 42	41	73	20 23	40	72	21 03	40	71	21 43	40	70	272
89	11 25	42	80	12 07	42	79	12 49	42	79	13 31	42	78	14 13	42	77	14 55	42	77	15 37	41	76	16 18	42	75	17 00	41	74	17 41	41	74	18 22	40	73	19 02	41	72	19 43	40	71	20 23	41	70	21 04	40	70	271
90	10 44	+42	80	11 26	+42	79	12 08	+43	78	12 51	+42	77	13 33	+42	77	14 15	+41	76	14 56	+42	75	15 38	+41	74	16 19	+42	74	17 01	+41	73	17 42	+41	72	18 23	+41	71	19 04	+40	71	19 44	+41	70	20 25	+40	69	270
91	10 03	42	79	10 45	43	78	11 28	42	77	12 10	42	77	12 52	42	76	13 34	42	75	14 16	42	74	14 58	42	74	15 40	41	73	16 21	41	72	17 02	42	71	17 44	40	71	18 24	41	70	19 05	41	69	19 46	40	68	269
92	09 22	43	78	10 05	42	77	10 47	43	77	11 30	42	76	12 12	42	75	12 54	42	75	13 36	42	74	14 18	42	73	15 00	41	72	15 41	42	72	16 23	41	71	17 04	41	70	17 45	41	69	18 26	41	69	19 07	41	68	268
93	08 41	43	77	09 24	43	77	10 07	42	76	10 49	43	75	11 32	42	75	12 14	42	74	12 56	42	73	13 38	42	72	14 20	42	72	15 02	42	71	15 44	41	70	16 25	42	69	17 07	41	69	17 48	41	68	18 29	41	67	267
94	08 01	43	77	08 44	42	76	09 26	43	75	10 09	43	75	10 52	42	74	11 34	42	73	12 16	43	72	12 59	42	72	13 41	42	71	14 23	42	70	15 05	41	69	15 46	42	69	16 28	41	68	17 09	41	67	17 50	42	66	266
95	07 20	+43	76	08 03	+43	75	08 46	+43	75	09 29	+43	74	10 12	+42	73	10 54	+43	72	11 37	+42	72	12 19	+42	71	13 01	+43	70	13 44	+42	70	14 26	+42	69	15 08	+41	68	15 49	+42	67	16 31	+41	67	17 12	+42	66	265
96	06 40	43	75	07 23	43	75	08 06	43	74	08 49	43	73	09 32	43	73	10 15	42	72	10 57	43	71	11 40	42	70	12 22	43	70	13 05	42	69	13 47	42	68	14 29	42	67	15 11	42	67	15 53	41	66	16 34	42	65	264
97	06 00	43	75	06 43	43	74	07 26	43	73	08 09	43	73	08 52	43	72	09 35	43	71	10 18	43	70	11 01	42	70	11 43	43	69	12 26	42	68	13 08	43	68	13 51	42	67	14 33	42	66	15 15	42	65	15 57	41	65	263
98	05 20	43	74	06 03	43	73	06 46	43	73	07 29	44	72	08 13	43	71	08 56	43	70	09 39	43	70	10 22	42	69	11 04	43	68	11 47	43	68	12 30	42	67	13 12	43	66	13 55	42	65	14 37	42	65	15 19	42	64	262
99	04 39	44	73	05 23	44	73	06 07	43	72	06 50	43	71	07 33	44	70	08 17	43	70	09 00	43	69	09 43	43	68	10 26	43	68	11 09	43	67	11 52	42	66	12 34	43	65	13 17	42	65	13 59	43	64	14 42	42	63	261
100	04 00	+43	72	04 43	+44	72	05 27	+44	71	06 11	+43	70	06 54	+44	70	07 38	+43	69	08 21	+43	68	09 04	+43	68	09 47	+44	67	10 31	+43	66	11 14	+43	66	11 57	+42	65	12 39	+43	64	13 22	+43	63	14 05	+42	63	260
101	03 20	44	72	04 04	44	71	04 48	43	70	05 31	44	70	06 15	44	69	06 59	43	68	07 42	44	68	08 26	43	67	09 09	44	66	09 53	43	66	10 36	43	65	11 19	43	64	12 02	43	63	12 45	43	63	13 28	43	62	259
102	02 41	43	71	03 24	44	70	04 08	44	70	04 52	44	69	05 36	44	68	06 20	44	68	07 04	44	67	07 48	43	66	08 31	44	66	09 15	43	65	09 58	44	64	10 42	43	64	11 25	43	63	12 08	43	62	12 51	43	61	258
103	02 01	44	70	02 45	44	70	03 29	44	69	04 13	45	68	04 58	44	68	05 42	44	67	06 26	43	66	07 09	44	66	07 53	44	65	08 37	44	64	09 21	43	64	10 04	44	63	10 48	43	62	11 31	44	61	12 15	43	61	257
104	01 22	44	70	02 06	45	69	02 51	44	68	03 35	44	68	04 19	44	67	05 03	45	66	05 48	44	66	06 32	44	65	07 16	44	64	08 00	44	64	08 44	43	63	09 27	44	62	10 11	44	61	10 55	43	61	11 38	44	60	256
105	00 43	+45	69	01 28	+44	68	02 12	+44	68	02 56	+45	67	03 41	+44	66	04 25	+45	66	05 10	+44	65	05 54	+44	64	06 38	+44	64	07 22	+45	63	08 07	+44	62	08 51	+44	62	09 35	+44	61	10 19	+43	60	11 02	+44	59	255
106	00 04	45	68	00 49	45	68	01 34	44	67	02 18	45	66	03 03	44	66	03 47	45	65	04 32	45	64	05 17	44	64	06 01	44	63	06 45	45	62	07 30	44	62	08 14	44	61	08 58	45	60	09 43	44	59	10 27	44	59	254
107	-0 34	44	67	00 10	45	67	00 55	45	66	01 40	45	65	02 25	45	65	03 10	45	64	03 55	44	63	04 39	45	63	05 24	45	62	06 09	44	62	06 53	45	61	07 38	44	60	08 22	45	60	09 07	44	59	09 51	44	58	253
108	-1 13	45	67	-0 28	45	66	00 17	45	65	01 02	45	65	01 47	45	64	02 32	45	63	03 17	45	63	04 02	45	62	04 47	45	61	05 32	45	61	06 17	45	60	07 02	45	60	07 47	44	59	08 31	45	58	09 16	44	57	252
109	-1 51	45	66	-1 06	46	65	-0 20	45	65	00 25	45	64	01 10	45	63	01 55	45	63	02 40	46	62	03 26	45	61	04 11	45	61	04 56	45	60	05 41	45	59	06 26	45	59	07 11	45	58	07 56	45	57	08 41	45	57	251
110	-2 29	+45	65	-1 44	+46	65	-0 58	+45	64	-0 13	+46	63	00 33	+45	63	01 18	+46	62	02 04	+45	61	02 49	+46	61	03 35	+45	60	04 20	+45	59	05 05	+46	59	05 51	+45	58	06 36	+45	57	07 21	+45	57	08 06	+45	56	250
111	-3 07	46	65	-2 21	46	64	-1 35	45	63	-0 50	46	63	-0 04	46	62	00 42	45	61	01 27	46	61	02 13	46	60	02 59	45	59	03 44	46	59	04 30	45	58	05 15	46	57	06 01	45	57	06 46	46	56	07 32	45	55	249
112	-3 44	46	64	-2 58	45	63	-2 13	46	63	-1 27	46	62	-0 41	46	61	00 05	46	61	00 51	46	60	01 37	46	59	02 23	46	59	03 09	46	58	03 55	45	57	04 40	46	57	05 26	46	56	06 12	46	55	06 58	45	55	248
113	-4 22	47	63	-3 35	46	62	-2 49	46	62	-2 03	46	61	-1 17	46	61	-0 31	46	60	00 15	46	59	01 01	46	59	01 47	46	58	02 33	47	57	03 20	46	57	04 06	46	56	04 52	46	55	05 38	46	55	06 24	46	54	247
114	-4 59	47	62	-4 12	46	62	-3 26	46	61	-2 40	47	60	-1 53	46	60	-1 07	46	59	-0 21	47	59	00 26	46	58	01 12	47	57	01 59	46	57	02 45	46	56	03 31	46	55	04 17	47	55	05 04	46	54	05 50	46	53	246
115	-5 35	+46	62	-4 49	+47	61	-4 02	+46	60	-3 16	+47	60	-2 29	+46	59	-1 43	+47	58	-0 56	+47	58	-0 09	+46	57	00 37	+47	57	01 24	+46	56	02 10	+47	55	02 57	+47	55	03 44	+46	54	04 30	+47	53	05 17	+46	53	245
116	-6 12	47	61	-5 25	47	60	-4 38	46	60	-3 52	47	59	-3 05	47	58	-2 18	47	58	-1 31	47	57	-0 44	47	56	00 03	46	56	00 49	47	55	01 36	47	55	02 23	47	54	03 10	47	53	03 57	47	53	04 44	46	52	244
117				-6 01	47	59	-5 14	47	59	-4 27	47	58	-3 40	47	58	-2 53	47	57	-2 06	47	56	-1 19	47	56	-0 32	47	55	00 15	48	54	01 03	47	54	01 50	47	53	02 37	47	53	03 24	47	52	04 11	47	51	243
118							-5 50	47	58	-5 03	48	57	-4 15	47	57	-3 28	47	56	-2 41	48	56	-1 53	47	55	-1 06	48	54	-0 18	47	54	00 29	47	53	01 16	48	53	02 04	47	52	02 51	47	51	03 38	48	51	242
119										-5 38	48	57	-4 50	48	56	-4 02	47	55	-3 15	48	55	-2 27	48	54	-1 39	47	54	-0 52	48	53	-0 04	47	52	00 43	48	52	01 31	48	51	02 19	47	51	03 06	48	50	241
120													-5 24	+47	55	-4 37	+48	55	-3 49	+48	54	-3 01	+48	54	-2 13	+48	53	-1 25	+48	52	-0 37	+48	52	00 11	+48	51	00 59	+48	51	01 47	+48	50	02 35	+47	49	240
121													-5 59	49	55	-5 10	48	54	-4 22	48	53	-3 34	48	53	-2 46	48	52	-1 58	48	52	-1 10	49	51	-0 21	48	50	00 27	48	50	01 15	48	49	02 03	48	49	239
122																-5 44	48	53	-4 56	49	53	-4 07	48	52	-3 19	49	51	-2 30	48	51	-1 42	49	50	-0 53	48	50	-0 05	49	49	00 44	48	48	01 32	49	48	238
123																			-5 29	49	52	-4 40	49	51	-3 51	49	51	-3 02	48	50	-2 14	49	50	-1 25	49	49	-0 36	49	48	00 13	48	48	01 01	50	47	237
124																			-6 01	49	51	-5 12	49	50	-4 23	49	50	-3 34	49	49	-2 45	49	49	-1 56	49	48	-1 07	49	48	-0 18	49	47	00 31	49	46	236
125																						-5 44	+49	50	-4 55	+49	49	-4 06	+50	49	-3 16	+49	48	-2 27	+49	47	-1 38	+50	47	-0 48	+49	46	00 01	+49	46	235
126																									-5 26	49	48	-4 37	50	48	-3 47	49	47	-2 58	50	47	-2 08	50	46	-1 18	49	46	-0 29	50	45	234
127																									-5 57	49	48	-5 08	50	47	-4 18	50	47	-3 28	50	46	-2 38	50	45	-1 48	50	45	-0 58	50	44	233
128																												-5 38	50	46	-4 48	50	46	-3 58	51	45	-3 07	50	45	-2 17	50	44	-1 27	50	44	232
129																															-5 17	50	45	-4 27	50	44	-3 37	51	44	-2 46	50	43	-1 56	51	43	231
130																															-5 47	+51	44	-4 56	+51	44	-4 05	+51	43	-3 14	+50	43	-2 24	+51	42	230
131																																		-5 25	51	43	-4 34	51	42	-3 43	52	42	-2 51	51	41	229
132																																		-5 53	51	42	-5 02	52	42	-4 10	51	41	-3 19	52	41	228
133																																					-5 29	52	41	-4 37	51	40	-3 46	52	40	227
134																																								-5 04	52	40	-4 12	52	39	226
135																																								-5 31	+53	39	-4 38	+52	38	225
136																																											-5 04	53	38	224
137																																											-5 29	53	37	223

DECLINATION (15°-29°) CONTRARY NAME TO LATITUDE

S. Lat. {LHA greater than 180°........ Zn=180−Z; LHA less than 180°.......... Zn=180+Z}

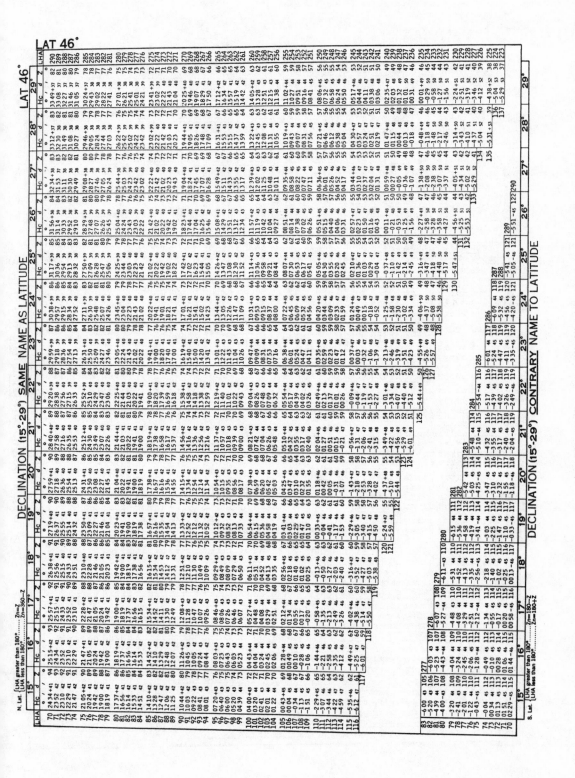

LHA	15° Hc	d	Z	16° Hc	d	Z	17° Hc	d	Z	18° Hc	d	Z	19° Hc	d	Z	20° Hc	d	Z	21° Hc	d	Z	22° Hc	d	Z	23° Hc	d	Z	24° Hc	d	Z	25° Hc	d	Z	26° Hc	d	Z	LHA
83	-6 00	43	105																																		277
82	-5 20	43	106	-6 03	43	107																															278
81	-4 39	44	107	-5 23	44	107	-6 07	43	108																												279
80	-4 00	-43	108	-4 43	-44	108	-5 27	-44	109	-6 11	-43	110																									280
79	-3 20	44	108	-4 04	44	109	-4 48	43	110	-5 31	44	110	-6 15	44	111																						281
78	-2 41	43	109	-3 24	44	110	-4 08	44	110	-4 52	44	111	-5 36	44	112																						282
77	-2 01	44	110	-2 45	44	110	-3 29	44	111	-4 13	45	112	-4 58	44	112	-5 42	44	113																			283
76	-1 22	44	110	-2 06	45	111	-2 51	44	112	-3 35	44	112	-4 19	44	113	-5 03	45	114	-5 48	44	114																284
75	-0 43	-45	111	-1 28	-44	112	-2 12	-44	112	-2 56	-45	113	-3 41	-44	114	-4 25	-45	114	-5 10	-44	115	-5 54	-44	116													285
74	-0 04	45	112	-0 49	45	112	-1 34	44	113	-2 18	45	114	-3 03	44	114	-3 47	45	115	-4 32	45	116	-5 17	44	116	-6 01	44	117										286
73	00 34	44	113	-0 10	45	113	-0 55	45	114	-1 40	45	115	-2 25	45	115	-3 10	45	116	-3 55	44	117	-4 39	45	117	-5 24	45	118	-6 09	44	118							287
72	01 13	45	113	00 28	45	114	-0 17	45	115	-1 02	45	115	-1 47	45	116	-2 32	45	117	-3 17	45	117	-4 02	45	118	-4 47	45	119	-5 32	45	119							288
71	01 51	45	114	01 06	46	115	00 20	45	115	-0 25	45	116	-1 10	45	117	-1 55	45	117	-2 40	46	118	-3 26	45	119	-4 11	45	119	-4 56	45	120	-5 41	45	121				289
70	02 29	-45	115	01 44	-46	115	00 58	-45	116	00 13	-46	117	-0 33	-45	117	-1 18	-46	118	-2 04	-45	119	-2 49	-46	119	-3 35	-45	120	-4 20	-45	121	-5 05	-46	121	-5 51	-45	122	290

N. Lat. {LHA greater than 180°........ Zn=Z; LHA less than 180°........... Zn=360−Z}

DECLINATION (0°-14°) CONTRARY NAME TO LATITUDE

LAT 46°

LHA	0° Hc	d	Z	1° Hc	d	Z	2° Hc	d	Z	3° Hc	d	Z	4° Hc	d	Z
	° ′	′	°	° ′	′	°	° ′	′	°	° ′	′	°	° ′	′	°
69	14 25	45	105	13 40	44	106	12 56	45	107	12 11	45	108	11 26	45	108
68	15 05	45	106	14 20	45	107	13 35	45	108	12 50	45	108	12 05	45	109
67	15 45	45	107	15 00	45	108	14 15	45	108	13 30	45	109	12 45	46	110
66	16 25	45	108	15 40	45	108	14 55	46	109	14 09	45	110	13 24	46	111
65	17 04	−45	109	16 19	−45	109	15 34	−46	110	14 48	−45	111	14 03	−46	111
64	17 44	46	109	16 58	45	110	16 13	46	111	15 27	46	111	14 41	45	112
63	18 23	46	110	17 37	45	111	16 52	46	112	16 06	46	112	15 20	46	113
62	19 02	46	111	18 16	46	112	17 30	46	112	16 44	46	113	15 58	46	114
61	19 41	46	112	18 55	46	112	18 09	46	113	17 23	47	114	16 36	46	114
60	20 19	−46	113	19 33	−46	113	18 47	−46	114	18 01	−47	115	17 14	−46	115
59	20 58	46	113	20 12	47	114	19 25	46	115	18 39	47	115	17 52	47	116
58	21 36	46	114	20 50	47	115	20 03	47	116	19 16	47	116	18 29	47	117
57	22 14	47	115	21 27	47	116	20 40	47	116	19 53	47	117	19 06	47	118
56	22 52	47	116	22 05	47	117	21 18	48	117	20 30	47	118	19 43	48	119
55	23 29	−47	117	22 42	−48	117	21 54	−47	118	21 07	−48	119	20 19	−47	119
54	24 06	47	118	23 19	48	118	22 31	48	119	21 43	47	120	20 56	48	120
53	24 43	48	119	23 55	48	119	23 07	48	120	22 19	48	120	21 31	48	121
52	25 19	48	119	24 31	48	120	23 43	48	121	22 55	48	121	22 07	49	122
51	25 55	48	120	25 07	48	121	24 19	48	122	23 31	49	122	22 42	49	123
50	26 31	−48	121	25 43	−49	122	24 54	−48	122	24 06	−49	123	23 17	−49	124
49	27 07	49	122	26 18	49	123	25 29	48	123	24 41	50	124	23 51	49	125
48	27 42	49	123	26 53	49	124	26 04	49	124	25 15	49	125	24 26	50	126
47	28 17	49	124	27 28	50	125	26 38	49	125	25 49	50	126	24 59	49	126
46	28 51	49	125	28 02	50	125	27 12	49	126	26 23	50	127	25 33	50	127
45	29 25	−49	126	28 36	−50	126	27 46	−50	127	26 56	−50	128	26 06	−51	128
44	29 59	50	127	29 09	50	127	28 19	50	128	27 29	51	129	26 38	50	129
43	30 32	50	128	29 42	51	128	28 51	50	129	28 01	51	130	27 10	51	130
42	31 05	51	129	30 14	50	129	29 24	51	130	28 33	51	131	27 42	51	131
41	31 37	51	130	30 46	51	130	29 55	51	131	29 04	51	131	28 13	51	132
40	32 09	−51	131	31 18	−51	131	30 27	−52	132	29 35	−51	132	28 44	−52	133
39	32 40	51	132	31 49	51	132	30 58	52	133	30 06	52	133	29 14	52	134
38	33 11	51	133	32 20	52	133	31 28	52	134	30 36	52	134	29 44	53	135
37	33 42	52	134	32 50	52	134	31 58	53	135	31 05	52	135	30 13	53	136
36	34 12	53	135	33 19	52	135	32 27	53	136	31 34	52	137	30 42	53	137
35	34 41	−53	136	33 48	−52	136	32 56	−53	137	32 03	−53	138	31 10	−53	138
34	35 10	53	137	34 17	53	137	33 24	53	138	32 31	54	139	31 37	53	139
33	35 38	53	138	34 45	53	139	33 52	54	139	32 58	54	140	32 04	53	140
32	36 06	54	139	35 12	53	140	34 19	54	140	33 25	54	141	32 31	54	141
31	36 33	54	140	35 39	54	141	34 45	54	141	33 51	54	142	32 57	55	142
30	36 59	−54	141	36 05	−54	142	35 11	−55	142	34 16	−54	143	33 22	−55	143
29	37 25	55	142	36 30	54	143	35 36	55	143	34 41	55	144	33 46	54	144
28	37 50	55	144	36 55	55	144	36 00	55	145	35 05	55	145	34 10	55	146
27	38 14	55	145	37 19	55	145	36 24	55	146	35 29	55	146	34 34	56	147
26	38 38	55	146	37 43	56	146	36 47	55	147	35 52	56	147	34 56	56	148
25	39 01	−55	147	38 06	−56	148	37 10	−56	148	36 14	−56	149	35 18	−56	149
24	39 23	55	148	38 28	56	149	37 32	57	149	36 35	56	150	35 39	56	150
23	39 45	56	150	38 49	56	150	37 53	57	150	36 56	56	151	36 00	57	151
22	40 06	57	151	39 09	56	151	38 13	57	152	37 16	57	152	36 19	56	152
21	40 26	57	152	39 29	57	152	38 32	57	153	37 35	57	153	36 38	57	154
20	40 45	−57	153	39 48	−57	154	38 51	−57	154	37 54	−57	154	36 57	−58	155
19	41 03	57	154	40 06	57	155	39 09	58	155	38 11	57	156	37 14	58	156
18	41 21	57	156	40 24	58	156	39 26	58	156	38 28	57	157	37 31	58	157
17	41 38	58	157	40 40	58	157	39 42	58	158	38 44	58	158	37 46	58	158
16	41 54	58	158	40 56	58	159	39 58	59	159	38 59	58	159	38 01	58	160
15	42 09	−59	160	41 10	−58	160	40 12	−58	160	39 14	−59	161	38 15	−58	161
14	42 23	59	161	41 24	58	161	40 26	59	162	39 27	58	162	38 29	59	162
13	42 36	59	162	41 37	58	163	40 39	59	163	39 40	59	163	38 41	59	163
12	42 48	59	164	41 49	59	164	40 50	58	164	39 52	59	164	38 53	59	165
11	43 00	59	165	42 01	60	165	41 01	59	165	40 02	59	166	39 03	59	166
10	43 10	−59	166	42 11	−59	167	41 12	−60	167	40 12	−59	167	39 13	−59	167
9	43 19	59	168	42 20	59	168	41 21	60	168	40 21	59	168	39 22	59	168
8	43 28	60	169	42 28	59	169	41 29	60	169	40 29	59	170	39 30	60	170
7	43 35	59	170	42 36	60	171	41 36	59	171	40 37	60	171	39 37	60	171
6	43 42	60	172	42 42	60	172	41 42	59	172	40 43	60	172	39 43	60	172
5	43 47	−59	173	42 48	−60	173	41 48	−60	173	40 48	−60	173	39 48	−60	174
4	43 52	60	174	42 52	60	175	41 52	60	175	40 52	60	175	39 52	59	175
3	43 56	60	176	42 56	60	176	41 56	60	176	40 56	60	176	39 56	60	176
2	43 58	60	177	42 58	60	177	41 58	60	177	40 58	60	177	39 58	60	177
1	44 00	60	179	43 00	60	179	42 00	60	179	41 00	60	179	40 00	60	179
0	44 00	−60	180	43 00	−60	180	42 00	−60	180	41 00	−60	180	40 00	−60	180

LHA	5° Hc	d	Z	6° Hc	d	Z	7° Hc	d	Z	8° Hc	d	Z	9° Hc	d	Z
	° ′	′	°	° ′	′	°	° ′	′	°	° ′	′	°	° ′	′	°
69	10 41	45	109	09 56	46	110	09 10	45	110	08 25	45	111	07 40	46	112
68	11 20	45	110	10 35	46	110	09 49	45	111	09 04	45	112	08 19	46	112
67	11 59	45	110	11 14	46	111	10 28	45	112	09 43	46	112	08 57	46	113
66	12 38	45	111	11 53	46	112	11 07	46	113	10 21	46	113	09 35	46	114
65	13 17	−46	112	12 31	−46	113	11 45	−46	113	10 59	−46	114	10 13	−46	115
64	13 56	46	113	13 10	46	113	12 24	47	114	11 37	46	115	10 51	46	115
63	14 34	46	114	13 48	47	114	13 01	46	115	12 15	46	116	11 29	47	116
62	15 12	46	114	14 26	47	115	13 39	46	116	12 53	47	116	12 06	47	117
61	15 50	47	115	15 03	46	116	14 17	47	116	13 30	47	117	12 43	47	118
60	16 28	−47	116	15 41	−47	117	14 54	−47	117	14 07	−47	118	13 20	−47	119
59	17 05	47	117	16 18	47	117	15 31	47	118	14 44	48	119	13 56	47	119
58	17 42	47	118	16 55	48	118	16 07	47	119	15 20	48	120	14 32	47	120
57	18 19	48	118	17 31	47	119	16 44	48	120	15 56	48	120	15 08	48	121
56	18 55	47	119	18 08	48	120	17 20	48	121	16 32	48	121	15 44	48	122
55	19 32	−48	120	18 44	−48	121	17 56	−48	121	17 08	−49	122	16 19	−48	123
54	20 08	49	121	19 19	48	122	18 31	48	122	17 43	49	123	16 54	48	123
53	20 43	48	122	19 55	49	122	19 06	48	123	18 18	49	124	17 29	49	124
52	21 18	48	123	20 30	49	123	19 41	49	124	18 52	49	124	18 03	49	125
51	21 53	48	124	21 05	50	124	20 15	49	125	19 26	49	125	18 37	49	126
50	22 28	−49	124	21 39	−49	125	20 50	−50	126	20 00	−49	126	19 11	−50	127
49	23 02	49	125	22 13	50	126	21 23	49	126	20 34	50	127	19 44	50	128
48	23 36	50	126	22 46	49	127	21 57	50	127	21 07	50	128	20 17	50	129
47	24 10	50	127	23 20	50	128	22 30	51	128	21 39	50	129	20 49	50	129
46	24 43	51	128	23 52	50	129	23 02	50	129	22 12	51	130	21 21	51	130
45	25 15	−50	129	24 25	−51	129	23 34	−50	130	22 44	−51	131	21 53	−51	131
44	25 48	51	130	24 57	51	130	24 06	51	131	23 15	51	132	22 24	51	132
43	26 19	51	131	25 28	51	131	24 37	51	132	23 46	51	132	22 55	52	133
42	26 51	52	132	25 59	51	132	25 08	52	133	24 16	51	133	23 25	52	134
41	27 22	52	133	26 30	52	133	25 38	51	134	24 47	52	134	23 55	52	135
40	27 52	−52	134	27 00	−52	134	26 08	−52	135	25 16	−52	135	24 24	−52	136
39	28 22	52	135	27 30	52	135	26 38	53	136	25 45	52	136	24 53	53	137
38	28 51	52	136	27 59	53	136	27 06	52	137	26 14	53	137	25 21	53	138
37	29 20	52	137	28 28	53	137	27 35	53	138	26 42	53	138	25 49	53	139
36	29 49	53	138	28 56	53	138	28 03	54	139	27 09	53	139	26 16	53	140
35	30 17	−54	139	29 23	−53	139	28 30	−54	140	27 36	−53	140	26 43	−54	141
34	30 44	54	140	29 50	53	140	28 57	54	141	28 03	54	141	27 09	54	142
33	31 11	54	141	30 17	54	141	29 23	54	142	28 29	55	142	27 34	54	143
32	31 37	54	142	30 43	55	142	29 48	54	143	28 54	55	143	27 59	54	144
31	32 02	54	143	31 08	55	143	30 13	54	144	29 19	55	144	28 24	55	145
30	32 27	−55	144	31 32	−54	144	30 38	−55	145	29 43	−55	145	28 48	−55	146
29	32 52	56	145	31 56	55	145	31 01	55	146	30 06	55	146	29 11	56	147
28	33 15	55	146	32 20	56	147	31 24	55	147	30 29	56	147	29 33	55	148
27	33 38	55	147	32 43	56	148	31 47	56	148	30 51	56	148	29 55	56	149
26	34 00	55	148	33 05	56	149	32 09	56	149	31 13	56	150	30 17	57	150
25	34 22	−56	149	33 26	−56	150	32 30	−57	150	31 33	−56	151	30 37	−56	151
24	34 43	56	151	33 47	57	151	32 50	56	151	31 54	57	152	30 57	57	152
23	35 03	57	152	34 06	56	152	33 10	57	152	32 13	57	153	31 16	57	153
22	35 23	57	153	34 26	57	153	33 29	57	154	32 32	57	154	31 35	58	154
21	35 41	57	154	34 44	57	154	33 47	57	155	32 50	58	155	31 52	57	155
20	35 59	−57	155	35 02	−58	156	34 04	−57	156	33 07	−58	156	32 09	−57	157
19	36 16	57	156	35 19	58	157	34 21	58	157	33 23	57	157	32 26	58	158
18	36 33	58	158	35 35	58	158	34 37	58	158	33 39	58	158	32 41	58	159
17	36 48	58	159	35 50	58	159	34 52	58	159	33 54	58	160	32 56	58	160
16	37 03	58	160	36 05	59	160	35 06	58	161	34 08	58	161	33 10	59	161
15	37 17	−58	161	36 19	−59	161	35 20	−59	162	34 21	−58	162	33 23	−59	162
14	37 30	59	162	36 31	58	163	35 33	59	163	34 34	59	163	33 35	59	163
13	37 42	59	164	36 43	58	164	35 45	59	164	34 46	59	164	33 47	59	165
12	37 54	59	165	36 55	59	165	35 56	59	165	34 57	59	166	33 58	60	166
11	38 04	59	166	37 05	59	166	36 06	59	166	35 07	60	167	34 07	59	167
10	38 14	−60	167	37 14	−59	168	36 15	−59	168	35 16	−60	168	34 16	−59	168
9	38 23	60	169	37 23	59	169	36 24	60	169	35 24	59	169	34 25	60	169
8	38 30	59	170	37 31	60	170	36 31	59	170	35 32	60	170	34 32	59	170
7	38 37	59	171	37 38	60	171	36 38	60	171	35 38	59	172	34 39	60	172
6	38 43	59	172	37 44	60	172	36 44	60	173	35 44	60	173	34 44	59	173
5	38 48	−59	174	37 49	−60	174	36 49	−60	174	35 49	−60	174	34 49	−60	174
4	38 53	60	175	37 53	60	175	36 53	60	175	35 53	60	175	34 53	60	175
3	38 56	60	176	37 56	60	176	36 56	60	176	35 56	60	176	34 56	60	176
2	38 58	60	177	37 58	60	178	36 58	60	178	35 58	60	178	34 58	60	178
1	39 00	60	179	38 00	60	179	37 00	60	179	36 00	60	179	35 00	60	179
0	39 00	−60	180	38 00	−60	180	37 00	−60	180	36 00	−60	180	35 00	−60	180

LHA	10° Hc	d	Z	11° Hc	d	Z	12° Hc	d	Z	13° Hc	d	Z	14° Hc	d	Z	LHA
	° ′	′	°	° ′	′	°	° ′	′	°	° ′	′	°	° ′	′	°	
69	06 54	45	112	06 09	46	113	05 23	45	114	04 38	46	114	03 52	45	115	291
68	07 33	46	113	06 47	45	114	06 02	46	114	05 16	46	115	04 30	46	116	292
67	08 11	46	114	07 25	45	114	06 40	46	115	05 54	46	116	05 08	46	116	293
66	08 49	46	114	08 03	46	115	07 17	46	116	06 31	46	116	05 45	46	117	294
65	09 27	−46	115	08 41	−46	116	07 55	−47	117	07 08	−46	117	06 22	−47	118	295
64	10 05	47	116	09 18	46	117	08 32	47	117	07 45	46	118	06 59	47	119	296
63	10 42	47	117	09 55	46	117	09 09	47	118	08 22	47	119	07 35	47	119	297
62	11 19	47	118	10 32	47	118	09 45	47	119	08 58	47	119	08 11	47	120	298
61	11 56	47	118	11 09	47	119	10 22	47	120	09 35	48	120	08 47	47	121	299
60	12 33	−48	119	11 45	−47	120	10 58	−48	120	10 10	−47	121	09 23	−48	122	300
59	13 09	48	120	12 21	47	121	11 34	48	121	10 46	48	122	09 58	48	122	301
58	13 45	48	121	12 57	48	121	12 09	48	122	11 21	48	123	10 33	48	123	302
57	14 20	48	122	13 32	48	122	12 44	48	123	11 56	48	123	11 08	48	124	303
56	14 56	48	122	14 08	49	123	13 19	48	124	12 31	49	124	11 42	48	125	304
55	15 31	−49	123	14 42	−48	124	13 54	−49	124	13 05	−49	125	12 16	−48	126	305
54	16 06	49	124	15 17	49	125	14 28	49	125	13 39	49	126	12 50	49	126	306
53	16 40	49	125	15 51	49	125	15 02	49	126	14 13	49	127	13 24	50	127	307
52	17 14	49	126	16 25	49	126	15 36	50	127	14 46	49	127	13 57	50	128	308
51	17 48	50	127	16 58	49	127	16 09	50	128	15 19	50	128	14 29	50	129	309
50	18 21	−50	127	17 31	−50	128	16 41	−49	129	15 52	−50	129	15 02	−51	130	310
49	18 54	50	128	18 04	50	129	17 14	50	129	16 24	51	130	15 33	50	131	311
48	19 27	51	129	18 36	50	130	17 46	51	130	16 55	50	131	16 05	51	131	312
47	19 59	51	130	19 08	50	131	18 18	51	131	17 27	51	132	16 36	51	132	313
46	20 30	50	131	19 40	51	131	18 49	51	132	17 58	51	133	17 07	52	133	314
45	21 02	−51	132	20 11	−52	132	19 19	−51	133	18 28	−51	133	17 37	−52	134	315
44	21 33	52	133	20 41	51	133	19 50	52	134	18 58	51	134	18 07	52	135	316
43	22 03	52	134	21 11	51	134	20 20	52	135	19 28	52	135	18 36	52	136	317
42	22 33	52	135	21 41	52	135	20 49	52	136	19 57	52	136	19 05	52	137	318
41	23 03	53	135	22 10	52	136	21 18	52	137	20 26	53	137	19 33	52	138	319
40	23 32	−53	136	22 39	−52	137	21 47	−53	137	20 54	−53	138	20 01	−53	138	320
39	24 00	53	137	23 07	53	138	22 14	52	138	21 22	53	139	20 29	54	139	321
38	24 28	53	138	23 35	53	139	22 42	53	139	21 49	54	140	20 55	53	140	322
37	24 56	54	139	24 02	53	140	23 09	54	140	22 15	53	141	21 22	54	141	323
36	25 23	54	140	24 29	54	141	23 35	53	141	22 42	54	142	21 48	54	142	324
35	25 49	−54	141	24 55	−54	142	24 01	−54	142	23 07	−54	143	22 13	−54	143	325
34	26 15	54	142	25 21	54	143	24 27	55	143	23 32	54	144	22 38	55	144	326
33	26 40	54	143	25 46	55	144	24 51	54	144	23 57	55	145	23 02	55	145	327
32	27 05	55	144	26 10	55	145	25 15	54	145	24 21	55	146	23 26	55	146	328
31	27 29	55	145	26 34	55	146	25 39	55	146	24 44	55	147	23 49	56	147	329
30	27 53	−56	146	26 57	−55	147	26 02	−55	147	25 07	−56	148	24 11	−55	148	330
29	28 15	55	147	27 20	56	148	26 24	55	148	25 29	56	148	24 33	56	149	331
28	28 38	56	148	27 42	56	149	26 46	56	149	25 50	56	150	24 54	56	150	332
27	28 59	56	149	28 03	56	150	27 07	56	150	26 11	56	151	25 15	56	151	333
26	29 20	56	150	28 24	56	151	27 28	57	151	26 31	56	152	25 35	57	152	334
25	29 41	−57	151	28 44	−56	152	27 48	−57	152	26 51	−57	153	25 54	−57	153	335
24	30 00	57	152	29 03	56	153	28 07	57	153	27 10	57	154	26 13	57	154	336
23	30 19	57	154	29 22	57	154	28 25	57	154	27 28	57	155	26 31	57	155	337
22	30 37	57	155	29 40	57	155	28 43	57	155	27 46	58	156	26 48	57	156	338
21	30 55	58	156	29 57	57	156	29 00	58	156	28 02	57	157	27 05	58	157	339
20	31 12	−58	157	30 14	−58	157	29 16	−57	157	28 19	−58	158	27 21	−58	158	340
19	31 28	58	158	30 30	58	158	29 32	58	159	28 34	58	159	27 36	58	159	341
18	31 43	58	159	30 45	58	159	29 47	58	160	28 49	59	160	27 50	58	160	342
17	31 58	59	160	30 59	58	160	30 01	58	161	29 03	59	161	28 04	58	161	343
16	32 11	58	161	31 13	59	162	30 14	58	162	29 16	59	162	28 17	58	162	344
15	32 24	−58	162	31 26	−59	163	30 27	−59	163	29 28	−58	163	28 30	−59	163	345
14	32 36	58	164	31 38	59	164	30 39	59	164	29 40	59	164	28 41	59	165	346
13	32 48	59	165	31 49	59	165	30 50	59	165	29 51	59	165	28 52	59	166	347
12	32 58	59	166	31 59	59	166	31 00	59	166	30 01	59	167	29 02	59	167	348
11	33 08	59	167	32 09	59	167	31 10	60	167	30 10	59	168	29 11	59	168	349
10	33 17	−59	168	32 18	−60	168	31 18	−59	169	30 19	−59	169	29 20	−60	169	350
9	33 25	59	169	32 26	60	170	31 26	59	170	30 27	60	170	29 27	59	170	351
8	33 33	60	171	32 33	60	171	31 33	59	171	30 34	60	171	29 34	60	171	352
7	33 39	60	172	32 39	59	172	31 40	60	172	30 40	60	172	29 40	60	172	353
6	33 45	60	173	32 45	60	173	31 45	60	173	30 45	60	173	29 45	59	173	354
5	33 49	−60	174	32 49	−59	174	31 50	−60	174	30 50	−60	174	29 50	−60	174	355
4	33 53	60	175	32 53	60	175	31 53	60	175	30 53	59	176	29 54	60	176	356
3	33 56	60	176	32 56	60	177	31 56	60	177	30 56	60	177	29 56	60	177	357
2	33 58	60	178	32 58	60	178	31 58	60	178	30 58	60	178	29 58	60	178	358
1	34 00	60	179	33 00	60	179	32 00	60	179	31 00	60	179	30 00	60	179	359
0	34 00	−60	180	33 00	−60	180	32 00	−60	180	31 00	−60	180	30 00	−60	180	360

S. Lat. {LHA greater than 180°....... Zn=180−Z; LHA less than 180°........... Zn=180+Z}

DECLINATION (0°-14°) CONTRARY NAME TO LATITUDE

Correction to Tabulated Altitude for Minutes of Declination

d/′	1	2	3	4	5	6	7	8	9	10	11	12	13	14	15	16	17	18	19	20	21	22	23	24	25	26	27	28	29	30	31	32	33	34	35	36	37	38	39	40	41	42	43	44	45	46	47	48	49	50	51	52	53	54	55	56	57	58	59	60	d/′
0	0	0	0	0	0	0	0	0	0	0	0	0	0	0	0	0	0	0	0	0	0	0	0	0	0	0	0	0	0	0	0	0	0	0	0	0	0	0	0	0	0	0	0	0	0	0	0	0	0	0	0	0	0	0	0	0	0	0	0	0	0
1	0	0	0	0	0	0	0	0	0	0	0	0	0	0	0	0	0	0	0	0	0	0	0	0	0	0	0	0	0	0	1	1	1	1	1	1	1	1	1	1	1	1	1	1	1	1	1	1	1	1	1	1	1	1	1	1	1	1	1	1	1
2	0	0	0	0	0	0	0	0	0	0	0	0	0	0	0	1	1	1	1	1	1	1	1	1	1	1	1	1	1	1	1	1	1	1	1	1	1	1	1	1	1	1	1	1	2	2	2	2	2	2	2	2	2	2	2	2	2	2	2	2	2
3	0	0	0	0	0	0	0	0	0	0	1	1	1	1	1	1	1	1	1	1	1	1	1	1	1	1	1	1	1	2	2	2	2	2	2	2	2	2	2	2	2	2	2	2	2	2	2	2	2	2	3	3	3	3	3	3	3	3	3	3	3
4	0	0	0	0	0	0	0	1	1	1	1	1	1	1	1	1	1	1	1	1	1	1	2	2	2	2	2	2	2	2	2	2	2	2	2	2	2	3	3	3	3	3	3	3	3	3	3	3	3	3	3	3	4	4	4	4	4	4	4	4	4
5	0	0	0	0	0	0	1	1	1	1	1	1	1	1	1	1	1	2	2	2	2	2	2	2	2	2	2	2	2	2	3	3	3	3	3	3	3	3	3	3	3	4	4	4	4	4	4	4	4	4	4	4	4	4	5	5	5	5	5	5	5
6	0	0	0	0	0	1	1	1	1	1	1	1	1	1	2	2	2	2	2	2	2	2	2	2	2	3	3	3	3	3	3	3	3	3	4	4	4	4	4	4	4	4	4	4	4	5	5	5	5	5	5	5	5	5	6	6	6	6	6	6	6
7	0	0	0	0	1	1	1	1	1	1	1	1	2	2	2	2	2	2	2	2	2	3	3	3	3	3	3	3	3	4	4	4	4	4	4	4	4	4	5	5	5	5	5	5	5	5	5	6	6	6	6	6	6	6	6	7	7	7	7	7	7
8	0	0	0	1	1	1	1	1	1	1	1	2	2	2	2	2	2	2	3	3	3	3	3	3	3	3	4	4	4	4	4	4	4	5	5	5	5	5	5	5	5	6	6	6	6	6	6	6	7	7	7	7	7	7	7	7	8	8	8	8	8
9	0	0	0	1	1	1	1	1	1	2	2	2	2	2	2	2	3	3	3	3	3	3	3	4	4	4	4	4	4	4	5	5	5	5	5	5	6	6	6	6	6	6	6	7	7	7	7	7	7	8	8	8	8	8	8	8	9	9	9	9	9
10	0	0	0	1	1	1	1	1	2	2	2	2	2	2	2	3	3	3	3	3	4	4	4	4	4	4	4	5	5	5	5	5	6	6	6	6	6	6	6	7	7	7	7	7	8	8	8	8	8	8	8	9	9	9	9	9	10	10	10	10	10
11	0	0	1	1	1	1	1	1	2	2	2	2	2	3	3	3	3	3	3	4	4	4	4	4	5	5	5	5	5	6	6	6	6	6	6	7	7	7	7	7	8	8	8	8	8	8	9	9	9	9	9	10	10	10	10	10	10	11	11	11	11
12	0	0	1	1	1	1	1	2	2	2	2	2	3	3	3	3	3	4	4	4	4	4	5	5	5	5	5	6	6	6	6	6	7	7	7	7	7	8	8	8	8	8	9	9	9	9	9	10	10	10	10	10	11	11	11	11	11	12	12	12	12
13	0	0	1	1	1	1	2	2	2	2	2	3	3	3	3	3	4	4	4	4	5	5	5	5	5	6	6	6	6	6	7	7	7	7	8	8	8	8	8	9	9	9	9	10	10	10	10	10	11	11	11	11	11	12	12	12	12	13	13	13	13
14	0	0	1	1	1	1	2	2	2	2	3	3	3	3	4	4	4	4	4	5	5	5	5	6	6	6	6	7	7	7	7	7	8	8	8	8	9	9	9	9	10	10	10	10	10	11	11	11	11	12	12	12	12	13	13	13	13	14	14	14	14
15	0	0	1	1	1	2	2	2	2	2	3	3	3	4	4	4	4	4	5	5	5	6	6	6	6	6	7	7	7	8	8	8	8	8	9	9	9	10	10	10	10	10	11	11	11	12	12	12	12	12	13	13	13	14	14	14	14	14	15	15	15
16	0	1	1	1	1	2	2	2	2	3	3	3	3	4	4	4	5	5	5	5	6	6	6	6	7	7	7	7	8	8	8	9	9	9	9	10	10	10	10	11	11	11	11	12	12	12	13	13	13	13	14	14	14	14	15	15	15	15	16	16	16
17	0	1	1	1	1	2	2	2	3	3	3	3	4	4	4	5	5	5	5	6	6	6	7	7	7	7	8	8	8	8	9	9	9	10	10	10	10	11	11	11	12	12	12	12	13	13	13	14	14	14	14	15	15	15	16	16	16	16	17	17	17
18	0	1	1	1	2	2	2	2	3	3	3	4	4	4	4	5	5	5	6	6	6	7	7	7	8	8	8	8	9	9	9	10	10	10	10	11	11	11	12	12	12	13	13	13	14	14	14	14	15	15	15	16	16	16	16	17	17	17	18	18	18
19	0	1	1	1	2	2	2	3	3	3	3	4	4	4	5	5	5	6	6	6	7	7	7	8	8	8	9	9	9	10	10	10	10	11	11	11	12	12	12	13	13	13	14	14	14	15	15	15	16	16	16	16	17	17	17	18	18	18	19	19	19
20	0	1	1	1	2	2	2	3	3	3	4	4	4	5	5	5	6	6	6	7	7	7	8	8	8	9	9	9	10	10	10	11	11	11	12	12	12	13	13	13	14	14	14	15	15	15	16	16	16	17	17	17	18	18	18	19	19	19	20	20	20
21	0	1	1	1	2	2	2	3	3	4	4	4	5	5	5	6	6	6	7	7	7	8	8	8	9	9	9	10	10	10	11	11	12	12	12	13	13	13	14	14	14	15	15	15	16	16	16	17	17	18	18	18	19	19	19	20	20	20	21	21	21
22	0	1	1	1	2	2	3	3	3	4	4	4	5	5	6	6	6	7	7	7	8	8	8	9	9	10	10	10	11	11	11	12	12	12	13	13	14	14	14	15	15	15	16	16	16	17	17	18	18	18	19	19	19	20	20	21	21	21	22	22	22
23	0	1	1	2	2	2	3	3	3	4	4	5	5	5	6	6	7	7	7	8	8	8	9	9	10	10	10	11	11	12	12	12	13	13	13	14	14	15	15	15	16	16	16	17	17	18	18	18	19	19	20	20	20	21	21	21	22	22	23	23	23
24	0	1	1	2	2	2	3	3	4	4	4	5	5	6	6	6	7	7	8	8	8	9	9	10	10	10	11	11	12	12	12	13	13	14	14	14	15	15	16	16	16	17	17	18	18	18	19	19	20	20	20	21	21	22	22	22	23	23	24	24	24
25	0	1	1	2	2	2	3	3	4	4	5	5	5	6	6	7	7	8	8	8	9	9	10	10	10	11	11	12	12	12	13	13	14	14	15	15	15	16	16	17	17	18	18	18	19	19	20	20	20	21	21	22	22	22	23	23	24	24	25	25	25
26	0	1	1	2	2	3	3	3	4	4	5	5	6	6	6	7	7	8	8	9	9	10	10	10	11	11	12	12	13	13	13	14	14	15	15	16	16	16	17	17	18	18	19	19	20	20	20	21	21	22	22	23	23	23	24	24	25	25	26	26	26
27	0	1	1	2	2	3	3	4	4	4	5	5	6	6	7	7	8	8	9	9	9	10	10	11	11	12	12	13	13	14	14	14	15	15	16	16	17	17	18	18	18	19	19	20	20	21	21	22	22	22	23	23	24	24	25	25	26	26	27	27	27
28	0	1	1	2	2	3	3	4	4	5	5	6	6	7	7	7	8	8	9	9	10	10	11	11	12	12	13	13	14	14	14	15	15	16	16	17	17	18	18	19	19	20	20	21	21	21	22	22	23	23	24	24	25	25	26	26	27	27	28	28	28
29	0	1	1	2	2	3	3	4	4	5	5	6	6	7	7	8	8	9	9	10	10	11	11	12	12	13	13	14	14	14	15	15	16	16	17	17	18	18	19	19	20	20	21	21	22	22	23	23	24	24	25	25	26	26	27	27	28	28	29	29	29
30	0	1	2	2	2	3	4	4	4	5	6	6	6	7	8	8	8	9	10	10	10	11	12	12	12	13	14	14	14	15	16	16	16	17	18	18	18	19	20	20	20	21	22	22	22	23	24	24	24	25	26	26	26	27	28	28	28	29	30	30	30
31	1	1	2	2	3	3	4	4	5	5	6	6	7	7	8	8	9	9	10	10	11	11	12	12	13	13	14	14	15	16	16	17	17	18	18	19	19	20	20	21	21	22	22	23	23	24	24	25	25	26	26	27	27	28	28	29	29	30	30	31	31
32	1	1	2	2	3	3	4	4	5	5	6	6	7	7	8	9	9	10	10	11	11	12	12	13	13	14	14	15	15	16	17	17	18	18	19	19	20	20	21	21	22	22	23	23	24	25	25	26	26	27	27	28	28	29	29	30	30	31	31	32	32
33	1	1	2	2	3	3	4	4	5	6	6	7	7	8	8	9	9	10	10	11	12	12	13	13	14	14	15	15	16	16	17	18	18	19	19	20	20	21	21	22	23	23	24	24	25	25	26	26	27	28	28	29	29	30	30	31	31	32	32	33	33
34	1	1	2	2	3	3	4	5	5	6	6	7	7	8	8	9	10	10	11	11	12	12	13	14	14	15	15	16	16	17	18	18	19	19	20	20	21	22	22	23	23	24	24	25	26	26	27	27	28	28	29	29	30	31	31	32	32	33	33	34	34
35	1	1	2	2	3	4	4	5	5	6	6	7	8	8	9	9	10	10	11	12	12	13	13	14	15	15	16	16	17	18	18	19	19	20	20	21	22	22	23	23	24	24	25	26	26	27	27	28	29	29	30	30	31	32	32	33	33	34	34	35	35
36	1	1	2	2	3	4	4	5	5	6	7	7	8	8	9	10	10	11	11	12	13	13	14	14	15	16	16	17	17	18	19	19	20	20	21	22	22	23	23	24	25	25	26	26	27	28	28	29	29	30	31	31	32	32	33	34	34	35	35	36	36
37	1	1	2	2	3	4	4	5	6	6	7	7	8	9	9	10	10	11	12	12	13	14	14	15	15	16	17	17	18	18	19	20	20	21	22	22	23	23	24	25	25	26	27	27	28	28	29	30	30	31	31	32	33	33	34	35	35	36	36	37	37
38	1	1	2	3	3	4	4	5	6	6	7	8	8	9	10	10	11	11	12	13	13	14	15	15	16	16	17	18	18	19	20	20	21	22	22	23	23	24	25	25	26	27	27	28	28	29	30	30	31	32	32	33	34	34	35	35	36	37	37	38	38
39	1	1	2	3	3	4	5	5	6	6	7	8	8	9	10	10	11	12	12	13	14	14	15	16	16	17	18	18	19	20	20	21	21	22	23	23	24	25	25	26	27	27	28	29	29	30	31	31	32	32	33	34	34	35	36	36	37	38	38	39	39
40	1	1	2	3	3	4	5	5	6	7	7	8	9	9	10	11	11	12	13	13	14	15	15	16	17	17	18	19	19	20	21	21	22	23	23	24	25	25	26	27	27	28	29	29	30	31	31	32	33	33	34	35	35	36	37	37	38	39	39	40	40
41	1	1	2	3	3	4	5	5	6	7	8	8	9	10	10	11	12	12	13	14	14	15	16	16	17	18	18	19	20	20	21	22	23	23	24	25	25	26	27	27	28	29	29	30	31	31	32	33	33	34	35	36	36	37	38	38	39	40	40	41	41
42	1	1	2	3	4	4	5	6	6	7	8	8	9	10	10	11	12	13	13	14	15	15	16	17	18	18	19	20	20	21	22	22	23	24	24	25	26	27	27	28	29	29	30	31	32	32	33	34	34	35	36	36	37	38	38	39	40	41	41	42	42
43	1	1	2	3	4	4	5	6	6	7	8	9	9	10	11	11	12	13	14	14	15	16	16	17	18	19	19	20	21	22	22	23	24	24	25	26	27	27	28	29	29	30	31	32	32	33	34	34	35	36	37	37	38	39	39	40	41	42	42	43	43
44	1	1	2	3	4	4	5	6	7	7	8	9	10	10	11	12	12	13	14	15	15	16	17	18	18	19	20	21	21	22	23	23	24	25	26	26	27	28	29	29	30	31	32	32	33	34	34	35	36	37	37	38	39	40	40	41	42	43	43	44	44
45	1	2	2	3	4	4	5	6	7	8	8	9	10	10	11	12	13	14	14	15	16	16	17	18	19	20	20	21	22	22	23	24	25	26	26	27	28	28	29	30	31	32	32	33	34	34	35	36	37	38	38	39	40	40	41	42	43	44	44	45	45
46	1	2	2	3	4	5	5	6	7	8	8	9	10	11	12	12	13	14	15	15	16	17	18	18	19	20	21	21	22	23	24	25	25	26	27	28	28	29	30	31	31	32	33	34	34	35	36	37	38	38	39	40	41	41	42	43	44	44	45	46	46
47	1	2	2	3	4	5	5	6	7	8	9	9	10	11	12	13	13	14	15	16	16	17	18	19	20	20	21	22	23	24	24	25	26	27	27	28	29	30	31	31	32	33	34	34	35	36	37	38	38	39	40	41	42	42	43	44	45	45	46	47	47
48	1	2	2	3	4	5	6	6	7	8	9	10	10	11	12	13	14	14	15	16	17	18	18	19	20	21	22	22	23	24	25	26	26	27	28	29	30	30	31	32	33	34	34	35	36	37	38	38	39	40	41	42	42	43	44	45	46	46	47	48	48
49	1	2	2	3	4	5	6	7	7	8	9	10	11	11	12	13	14	15	16	16	17	18	19	20	20	21	22	23	24	24	25	26	27	28	29	29	30	31	32	33	33	34	35	36	37	38	38	39	40	41	42	42	43	44	45	46	47	47	48	49	49
50	1	2	2	3	4	5	6	7	8	8	9	10	11	12	12	13	14	15	16	17	18	18	19	20	21	22	22	23	24	25	26	27	28	28	29	30	31	32	32	33	34	35	36	37	38	38	39	40	41	42	42	43	44	45	46	47	48	48	49	50	50
51	1	2	3	3	4	5	6	7	8	8	9	10	11	12	13	14	14	15	16	17	18	19	20	20	21	22	23	24	25	26	26	27	28	29	30	31	31	32	33	34	35	36	37	37	38	39	40	41	42	42	43	44	45	46	47	48	48	49	50	51	51
52	1	2	3	3	4	5	6	7	8	9	10	10	11	12	13	14	15	16	16	17	18	19	20	21	22	23	23	24	25	26	27	28	29	29	30	31	32	33	34	35	36	36	37	38	39	40	41	42	42	43	44	45	46	47	48	49	49	50	51	52	52
53	1	2	3	4	4	5	6	7	8	9	10	11	11	12	13	14	15	16	17	18	19	19	20	21	22	23	24	25	26	26	27	28	29	30	31	32	33	34	34	35	36	37	38	39	40	41	42	42	43	44	45	46	47	48	49	49	50	51	52	53	53
54	1	2	3	4	4	5	6	7	8	9	10	11	12	13	14	14	15	16	17	18	19	20	21	22	22	23	24	25	26	27	28	29	30	31	32	32	33	34	35	36	37	38	39	40	40	41	42	43	44	45	46	47	48	49	50	50	51	52	53	54	54
55	1	2	3	4	5	6	6	7	8	9	10	11	12	13	14	15	16	16	17	18	19	20	21	22	23	24	25	26	27	28	28	29	30	31	32	33	34	35	36	37	38	38	39	40	41	42	43	44	45	46	47	48	49	50	50	51	52	53	54	55	55
56	1	2	3	4	5	6	7	7	8	9	10	11	12	13	14	15	16	17	18	19	20	21	21	22	23	24	25	26	27	28	29	30	31	32	33	34	35	35	36	37	38	39	40	41	42	43	44	45	46	47	48	49	49	50	51	52	53	54	55	56	56
57	1	2	3	4	5	6	7	8	9	10	10	11	12	13	14	15	16	17	18	19	20	21	22	23	24	25	26	27	28	28	29	30	31	32	33	34	35	36	37	38	39	40	41	42	43	44	45	46	47	48	48	49	50	51	52	53	54	55	56	57	57
58	1	2	3	4	5	6	7	8	9	10	11	12	13	14	14	15	16	17	18	19	20	21	22	23	24	25	26	27	28	29	30	31	32	33	34	35	36	37	38	39	40	41	42	43	44	44	45	46	47	48	49	50	51	52	53	54	55	56	57	58	58
59	1	2	3	4	5	6	7	8	9	10	11	12	13	14	15	16	17	18	19	20	21	22	23	24	25	26	27	28	29	30	30	31	32	33	34	35	36	37	38	39	40	41	42	43	44	45	46	47	48	49	50	51	52	53	54	55	56	57	58	59	59